Owl Medicine

Life is filled
with wonderful messages...
Pay attention! (And have fun!)

To order additional copies of this book, contact:
Xlibris Corporation   or   Sage Bear Press, Inc.
1-888-7-XLIBRIS   (215) 766-0760
www.Xlibris.com/owlmedicine.html   www.sagebearpress.com
Orders@Xlibris.com

To Karl ~
Here's to # 4, whether we need it or not!

This is a true story.
Most of the names and places in this book,
as well as their identifying
characteristics, have been changed to protect
the privacy of those involved.

Acknowledgements

From the time I first began writing this book, many people have influenced my journey. My parents, Lois and Henry Guerke, had a tremendous impact upon who I am and how I have come to live my life. Although my mother is now in the realm of spirit, her influence continues to color much of my life, and for that I am and will be forever grateful.

Friends and family who've given me encouragement and well-placed nudges at crucial points in this process include Elaine Ferry, dear friend, wise-woman, herbalist, and healer; Jane Gallagher, Lois Gallagher, Ellen Gallagher Naughton, and Delia Gallagher, who openly embraced my ideas and gave me the best gift of all: family acceptance to truly be myself, which has allowed me to share with them the fun and excitement of living a magical life; Georgelle Hirliman, for her friendship, her intriguing astrological and tarot readings, and most of all, her extraordinary editorial skills (IMO, of course!); Tricia McCaffrey Maloney, who recommended the first book that got me started on this path; A. T., Nancy Hallowell, Janet Boddy, Marge Bailie, Linda Boyce, Marcia Atkinson, Kate Hannan & John Arntz of House of Coffee in Peddler's Village, Anne Lyons, Lauri Robbins, Rocco, Dana Loundas, and Kathleen Fargnoli—each of you has made a difference when it counted, which I deeply appreciate; and Henry Guerke (of the Pittsburgh Guerkes) for making me laugh, especially at Belvedere.

Special thanks to Laura Russo at St. Martin's Press for coming through for me when I needed it most, to Steven Wright, Amy Shannon, and Matt Stein of Xlibris for their patience and wonderful humor in dealing with my perfectionistic tendencies, to Rosemary Carroll for her enthusiasm, professionalism, and gift for photography . . . and to Joyce Clarkson, for her astounding ability to translate the cover I've imagined for so long into a captivating work of art.

Finally, I acknowledge and honor my family, my dear circle of men, Karl, Karl, Maximus and Sage. Karl Daniel, your courage and willingness to *live* and *manifest* your creative dreams never fails to inspire me. Maximus, your achievements in transmuting challenges into tremendous gifts fill me with pride and reinforce my conviction that you are, indeed, well-named. Sage, you are my prince, my Coyote-Boy. Your unconditional love and joyful heart are more precious to me than you'll ever know. And Karl . . . my very best friend, my love, my partner. Thank you for giving me the freedom and means to make this happen. I love you.

Owl Medicine

Lisa JG Weikel

Owl . . .

Magic,

Omens,

Time and space.

Does the truth emerge?
Casting out deception,
Silent flight,

Sacred Medicine Bird.

-poem preceding "Owl"
from *Medicine Cards*
by Jamie Sams and
David Carson

CHAPTER ONE

W e were almost home. In the waning light shed by the setting November sun, everything around us was cast in a bronze glow. The few leaves left on the branches of the surrounding trees crackled brown and crispy in the soft chilly breeze.

"I could watch a million sunsets and never get tired of them," I remarked to my husband, Karl, as we rounded the corner and headed north, only a half mile from our house.

"You always say that when we get here," he laughed, turning around to face the western sky once more before we entered the tunnel of trees lining the final phase of our walk. He walked backwards for a few steps, drinking in the colors reflecting off the flat platters of clouds piled curiously low on the horizon. The sun, not quite set, shone through horizontal gaps in the clouds, creating five distinct beams of light that blazed onto the earth.

"I know," I said, sighing deeply. "It's just that sunsets always seem to quiet me, somehow, in a way that nothing else does. Not music; not meditation. Nothing." I kicked a pebble and watched it skitter across the pavement and land with a plop in a shallow puddle cupped by dead leaves. "I think it's the colors," I said with a grin. Karl teased me often about my attraction to bright colors and shiny objects.

"No doubt," he murmured distractedly, lost in the sunset.

"This necklace really affects my energy. It's a little unsettling, but I think it's just power, the power of the piece itself," I said, unzipping my parka a bit so I could touch the animals, carved from turquoise, bone, and shell, snuggling warm against my skin. "I love having all these different creatures dancing around my neck."

"It's an awesome totem necklace, Lis," Karl commented, turning around so that he was walking forward again. "I'm really glad you finally gave in and bought it."

"Thanks for encouraging me. You know how much I struggled with spending that kind of money."

"I know, but it's not as if you bought it on impulse," Karl said, echoing his supportive words of yesterday when I'd again agonized over whether to buy it. "You've been tempted by that necklace for at least six months! I figure, if it still has such a strong attraction to you after all this time, then you're meant to get it. Besides," he added, "it's not like you to *want* to buy jewelry. There must be something special about it."

I held my hands out in front of me. He was right. Practically the only decoration I ever wore were the three rings I saw before me: my engagement and wedding rings on my left hand, and the small antique diamond of my grandmother's on my right. There was something undeniably special about this necklace, I thought to myself, the most obvious being the appreciable surge in energy I felt whenever I wore it. Every time I touched it, from the first moment I saw it last summer to yesterday, when I'd worn it all day at Catherine's seminar, my hands became noticeably warm and rosy and my entire body resonated with a curious sort of vibration.

"What did you make of things this weekend?" I asked Karl, referring to the seminar we'd attended at our friend Beth's house. One of the featured speakers had been Catherine, our teacher and the woman from whom I'd purchased my totem necklace.

"It was OK," Karl said, shrugging his shoulders. "I had a

good time. But most of the stuff that she lectured on was information we've already heard on her tapes."

"I thought so, too," I said, looking at Karl in surprise. "I was kind of disappointed that she didn't go over anything new."

"Me too," said Karl. "But maybe that's why we should be happy that we're studying with her on our own."

"I suppose you're right," I agreed, though unconvinced. We continued walking, silently lost to our own thoughts. It seemed like every time we tried to talk today our conversation went nowhere. I wondered if Karl noticed. "I've felt . . . ." I began, searching for the right word, ". . . *squirrelly* ever since we got home this afternoon. Crabby and edgy and, I don't know. Weird. Have you felt it?"

"I haven't felt the way I usually feel after we get together with Catherine," Karl admitted. "Instead of feeling excited and energized by our philosophical discussions, I feel let down; sort of edgy." He looked up at me, realizing that he'd just used the same word I had. "You're right! I feel edgy too. As if something's not right, but not obvious enough for me to put my finger on it."

"Yes! That's how I feel! And every once in a while today I've felt this strange foreboding creeping in at the edge of my thoughts. Almost as if I'm afraid of something," I said absently, shaking my head as if to clear the cobwebs.

"Hmm," Karl responded wordlessly. We were reaching the crest of the hill.

"Look!" I cried, as an odd figure swaying in the trees to my right suddenly caught my eye. "Is that an owl?" I asked, standing stock still in the center of the road, pointing toward the object that had snagged my attention.

"Where?" Karl asked in a whisper, straining to follow the direction of my finger. "Is it sitting on a branch?"

"No, no," I insisted, impatiently *willing* him to see what I could see. I broke into a trot and headed toward the side of the road. "Look!" I called to Karl over my shoulder. "Behind the telephone pole here," I said, gesturing. "I think it's . . . eew," I stopped short. "It's . . . hanging—upside down." Hackles rose, prickly and irritating, under my sweater.

"Oh," Karl said softly. He squinted toward the bulky figure hanging in the trees just off the shoulder of the road, readjusting his perspective to search for a *dead* owl.

As we stepped into the thicket, trying not to get our jackets caught in the brambles, we could see that the creature swinging ever so slightly in the evening breeze was in fact a Great Horned Owl.

"How awful!" I cried, the sight giving my chest a squeeze. I approached the figure cautiously, hoping against hope that there might be some life force left in the bird and that we'd be able to set it free.

"Geez, Lisa," said Karl from behind me. "Be careful. Is it still alive?"

"I don't think so," I said sadly. I picked up a stick and gently probed the bird near its extended wing to see if I could get a reaction. Nothing. We edged closer.

The owl had been trapped by a single, thin tendril of grapevine, which had become wrapped around the base of its right leg. The bird's prey, a small rabbit, lay dead at the base of the tree from which the owl now hung in limp lifelessness.

"Look at how big it is," Karl said in awe. Although the owl was hanging upside down above our heads, its left wing, extended to its fullest by gravity, reached down almost to the center of my chest. "You wonder how in the world it got snagged by a grapevine, of all things."

"Yeah, you wonder," I said, half to myself. This bird was gorgeous. Powerful. Although I knew little about owls, it appeared to have been a young adult raptor, brazenly confident of its power. I shivered, feeling strangely unsettled. "This makes me sick," I said out loud. "It feels like such a waste of life."

"It does feel like a waste, doesn't it?" Karl mused. "The rabbit died to feed the owl, but now even the rabbit's death was in vain." He shuddered. "It just doesn't seem right somehow."

"And imagine what a horrible death it must have endured,"

I said, reaching out to stroke the feathers on its extended wing. "How it must have struggled and fought to try to free itself." My eyes brimmed with tears. "Ugh!"

Karl looked up at the sky. "We better get going," he said. "I didn't bring a flashlight."

The sun had set completely and darkness was wrapping itself around us, despite the appearance of stars just starting to become visible.

"We're not going to leave it here, are we?" I asked, aghast at the thought.

"Why not? What in the world are we going to do with a dead bird, Lisa?" He sounded irritated, as if he were dealing with a small child who wanted something ridiculous.

"We can't just leave it here, *Karl*," I shot back at him in the same tone he'd used with me. "You said it yourself. The death of this bird is a waste." I looked at him, his features barely discernible in the growing darkness. "The least we can do is preserve it. We can't just let it hang here and rot." I paused. "That would be even more of a waste."

"You do what you want. I want to go home." Abruptly, he turned and started picking his way out of the brambles, jumping over the shallow ditch at the side of the road, back onto the roadway. I followed.

A prickly, uneasy silence clung to us as we strode home.

"What are the chances of finding an owl like that?" I demanded as we rounded the corner, our house a hundred yards ahead.

"I don't know," Karl grumbled. "Pretty slim, I guess."

I snorted. "Pretty slim? Isn't that a bit of an understatement?" I didn't give him a chance to answer. "There's a message here. The owl is bringing us a message, Karl. Can't you feel it?"

"I don't know, Lis," he said. I couldn't see his face, but I could hear his doubt.

"Well I *know*," I said, surprised at the adamant tone to my voice. "There's a message here, maybe even a warning; and that owl sacrificed its life to bring it to us. It would be wrong to allow it to rot, ignored and unheeded, by the side of the road."

CHAPTER TWO

Finding the owl, and then writing about it in my journal that evening, made me notice yet again my sense of unease. I had been feeling antsy all day, as had Karl, but neither of us had wanted to admit it. After all, we'd just met with Catherine this weekend—energy and enthusiasm should have been pulsing through us, as it had on so many other occasions after we'd personally experienced her lectures. But, as we'd touched upon during our walk, things felt different this time.

At the seminar yesterday I'd worn, and then purchased from Catherine, an intricately carved totem necklace. I'd seen it and tried it on two times prior to this weekend: once in the middle of the summer, when it was with some jewelry Catherine had sent to Beth, and another time, in early fall, when Beth and I had traveled to the opposite side of Philadelphia to visit with Catherine for an evening. During that visit, not only did I try the totem necklace on again (and notice the same 'buzz' from wearing it that I had the first time) but I also purchased, on Catherine's recommendation, a beautiful moonstone about the size of a nickel. Catherine told me that the moonstone would help me 'open up.' I took this to mean 'open up to my highest good, open up to new levels of consciousness,' so I bought it. For many months thereafter, I carried the stone with me virtually everywhere I went.

Prior to this weekend, though, I still had not been prepared to pay the price being asked for the totem necklace. Granted, a discount was being offered by Catherine because I was her student. And the necklace itself was truly one-of-a-kind. Indeed, every time I saw it I envisioned it being worn by a powerful shaman. Though I wanted to believe that I was that powerful person, I knew, deep down inside, that I wasn't—at least not yet. But I was drawn to the piece, almost irresistibly. Not usually a collector of jewelry, my strong attraction was curious. For hours at a time, it seemed, I could sit and gaze at the tiny fish, turtles, rabbits, foxes, and birds encircling the great turquoise bear that marked the center of the necklace.

Then came the lecture yesterday and yet another opportunity to see it—and touch it—again. I wore the necklace practically the entire day and noticed the appreciable surge in energy that I felt while wearing it. My hands became very warm almost instantly after putting it on, and my entire body seemed to resonate with a hum that I was surprised no one else could hear. That's when I seriously began thinking about making the purchase. The necklace was definitely 'charged' with some type of vibration, and I chose (without knowing I was making a choice at the time) to perceive it as a positive, higher one. Perhaps the stones out of which the animal fetishes were carved would also help quicken my energy, I reasoned. The necklace certainly seemed to call to me. Every time I took it off I felt a literal tug, almost as if a piece of elastic connected it to my heart chakra, urging me to put the magnificent piece back around my neck.

So I'd purchased it. I'd taken the plunge and made the decision last night that it wanted to come home with me. I temporarily hushed the nagging voice within by telling myself that somehow I would 'earn' the right to wear this powerful totem necklace.

As I recorded in my journal the details of my weekend, and wondered at the pervasive uneasiness in my heart, it never occurred to me that the owl and the necklace might be connected—or that the test had already begun.

CHAPTER THREE

Monday morning I woke feeling fearful and agitated. I had a new secretary beginning at work and I felt worried about having someone new and unfamiliar in my office. The feeling was very puzzling to me, since I found the woman I'd hired to be delightful during both her interview and the other times we'd spoken since then. And what an illogical thing to think anyway! Of course I didn't know her, but why was I feeling vulnerable in a situation over which I presumably had control?

By Wednesday, I was starting to doubt everything. Maybe I shouldn't have bought the totem necklace from Catherine. Maybe it was an impulse purchase and I'd bought it for all the wrong reasons. I felt silly and stupid for even imagining myself worthy of wearing such a powerful piece of ceremonial jewelry. Then again, at other times, I found myself wondering if Catherine had overcharged me.

Despite my anxiety, or perhaps because of it, I wore the necklace non-stop for several days in a row. This ornament came from my teacher, a woman who lectured often on discernment and the need to verify in one's own mind the integrity of anyone professing to be a teacher. And I knew, from my own experience and observation, that Catherine was a woman of keen intellect, with an extensive background of study in classical and esoteric thought, as well as undeniable psychic gifts and abilities. Surely

I could trust anything I purchased from her to be for my highest and best good?! Then why was I nagged by such a profound sense of conflict and uneasiness over this transaction and the necklace itself?

Snap out of it!, I told myself Friday evening as I sat on the covers of our double bed, again writing in my journal. Karl and the boys were all asleep and I was using this window of silence to snatch the whirling thoughts in my head and tame them by setting them out on the paper before me. As I wrote, I recognized that this week long torture of second-guessing myself was getting me nowhere. I decided to enjoy the almost electrically energizing feeling that still seemed to pulse out of the necklace, and turned my attention to recording the curious facts and reactions I'd collected as I investigated what to do with—and make of— 'my' owl.

Within a day or so of my discovery, I'd made a few phone calls and discovered that owls are a federally protected species, as are all raptors or birds of prey. In order to have the bird preserved, I needed to donate it to a learning institution such as a school or a museum. It is for this reason that a Great Horned Owl stands guard at the door of my sons' elementary school library.

Following up on my feeling that the bird was bringing me a message, I looked for clues from both conventional and unconventional sources. I faxed the tale of my discovery to Catherine, hoping that she would both provide me with her own interpretation and also suggest other areas of research that could shed light on the symbolic associations of this bird.

Much to my surprise, Catherine provided me with no personal insight whatsoever. Her response, sent by fax an hour or so following my plea for illumination, consisted of a terse sentence acknowledging my inquiry and a copy of a two-page synopsis from some sort of metaphysical encyclopedia describing the owl's primary powers as 'sight in darkness, watchfulness, clairvoyance and prophecy.' The article also stated that the spiritual qualities often associated with the owl are 'escape' and 'sight in darkness' (both literally and spiritually), but I didn't see how this had any connection to my life or experience, nor did Catherine offer any suggestions or possible interpretations.

I was disappointed in the paucity of information she sent me, since I knew that the message was almost certainly a metaphysical one as opposed to a purely physical or mundane one. I respected Catherine so much, though, that I felt myself feeling guilty for intruding upon her time with such a silly request, so I didn't press the issue. Although I was unaware of it at the time, Catherine and I would never discuss the subject of my finding the owl—or the message it brought—despite their ultimate significance to us both.

I was left, then, to my own resources, which mostly consisted of conventional encyclopedia articles and books on nature. As days and then weeks went by I learned, among other things, that death is often associated with the owl. Many American Indian tribes fear the hoot of the owl, because it signifies that death is close by or imminent.

There is also the traditional, mythological symbolism of Owl and its association with Athena, the goddess of Wisdom. Athena's owl sat on the goddess's left shoulder, giving her wise counsel as well as serving to 'light up her blind side.'

In telling my story of finding the owl, I was surprised when two different people spontaneously made comments about the 'warrior nature' of owls. These references had particular significance to me due to an adventure that Karl and I were scheduled to embark upon right after Christmas. None of the people who made the comments about the warrior aspect of the owl knew of our upcoming trip.

This is strange, I thought to myself as I reviewed my journal entry. *There's a message here, I just know it! But nothing fits. It seems like the message should be obvious, but it feels . . . obscured, as though I can't see it, no matter how hard I look. But that doesn't make sense either; the owl is supposed to help me see! Maybe I'm trying too hard. Or maybe I'm making it all up.*

Frustrated, I flipped my notebook closed and dropped it on the floor beside the bed. Turning off the light and snuggling under the covers, I resolved to stop thinking about the owl and its possible message, and just get on with my life.

CHAPTER FOUR

November blurred into December and I found myself caught up in handling my growing caseload. As I plodded through the gray December days, I noticed that I was persistently bothered by a pervasive sense of insecurity and 'being a failure.' It didn't make sense. Karl and the boys were healthy and happy. My law practice was expanding. My new secretary was working out nicely, despite my earlier apprehension. Gee, what more could I want?

"Ellen, I can't stand it," I said into the telephone to my good friend, as I sat in my office. "Why am I feeling such intense feelings of yuck toward myself?"

"Only you can answer that question, Lisa," said Ellen pragmatically. "The best thing I can suggest is for you to take some time out for yourself—right now—and meditate."

I hated it when either Ellen or Karl suggested meditation to me as an answer to my discomfort. They both seem so adept at it, engaging in that mode of spiritual practice on a regular basis, while I, on the other hand, resist it with a ferocious persistence and tenacity. I can't even figure out why I react so strongly to this particular discipline since I almost always feel better after I do it and virtually never feel worse. It just doesn't appeal to me, I guess.

Nevertheless, I recognized the wisdom in Ellen's suggestion

and agreed to give it a try. It helped that Ellen practically hung up on me when I told her that my secretary had left the office only a few minutes before in order to run an errand and get some lunch. We both knew she'd be gone for at least an hour. Ellen knew my tricks and wasn't about to let me spend the time talking to her when I could be meditating. She quickly made up some obvious excuse and left me hanging on the phone.

Oh well, I grumbled to myself. *I suppose it wouldn't kill me to sit quietly for at least a few minutes.* Grabbing a cushion off the wicker seat in my waiting room, I plopped myself onto the floor, crossed my legs, and began clearing my mind. As always, there was a constant stream of obnoxious chatter that tried valiantly to persuade me to knock this off, get up, and get on with my work. I ignored the chatter. I went deeper.

Suddenly, I was face to face with a rabbit staring straight into my eyes. Its ears were laying flat against its head and it was crouched down as though trying to make itself disappear. I was so surprised by this image that the chatter started up again and I decided to go back to work. The image made no sense to me whatsoever, and I shrugged off the entire episode as another twenty minutes wasted 'meditating' when I could have been doing something—anything—else.

When I got home that evening Ellen called me as I was preparing dinner. "Well?" she asked imperatively. "Did you meditate after we hung up?"

"Yes I did, as a matter of fact," I responded with some satisfaction. I was glad that I could answer affirmatively and, in the process, show her how ineffective a practice it was for me to engage in. "And all I got was this stark image of a dumb rabbit staring me straight in the face."

"A rabbit?" she asked. "Does that mean anything to you?"

"No, of course not," I said, dismissing her probe immediately. "I wrote it off as a meaningless figment of my imagination. It kind of irritated me, so I called it quits and went right back to work. In fact, I forgot about it completely until just now. I'd meant to look it up in the Medicine Cards when I got home, just in case they could help me make some sense out of the image, but instead I just started making dinner."

"Well think about it now," urged Ellen. "Have you seen any rabbits lately or anything?"

"I have absolutely no idea why a rabbit would appear to me in a meditation," I insisted. "I haven't seen any rabbits, and I don't think about rabbits—except…" My voice trailed off.

"What? Except what?" Ellen demanded.

"Except the rabbit that was caught by my owl. It never even occurred to me until just this second that a rabbit is the prey, or victim, of the owl!"

"Just a figure of your imagination, huh?" Ellen snorted. "Right. When are you going to start giving credence to the messages you get in meditation?" she chided.

"Oh come on," I shot back, refusing to admit that this made any sense whatsoever. "So what if I made a connection between the rabbit and the owl. What does it mean; that's the important thing! Am I supposed to think of myself as a victim, or what?" I was skeptical, to say the least, if not a little irritated by the suggestion that I might be a victim.

"Maybe you better take the time now to look up the meaning of rabbit in the animal cards," Ellen suggested in a more gentle tone, referring to the Medicine Cards® by Jamie Sams and David Carson, which she knew I'd borrowed from Beth only the day before. "Maybe that will give you a clue. And even if it doesn't," she continued, "I'm sure you can make some sense out of the connection if you just let yourself be quiet a while."

With that, Ellen hung up and I went upstairs to retrieve the cards. I'd stashed them on the floor beside my bed, intending to look at and play with them over the weekend. Dinner could wait. Maybe I *had* received a clue to understanding my recent feelings of inadequacy and failure.

Finding the section on "Rabbit," I settled onto the comforter on our bed, cross-legged. What I read hit me squarely between the eyes, though not until I recovered from seeing the drawing of the Rabbit staring out at me from the book. It was virtually identical to the image I'd seen in my meditation! But I hadn't played with the animal cards yet. How could I have imagined the same image as the one now staring me in the face? Then I started reading. The main idea or concept associated with Rabbit: *Fear.* But the first sentence spooked me into knowing that 'coincidence' should never again be a word in my vocabulary.

"A long time ago—no one really knows how long ago it was— Rabbit was a brave and fearless *warrior* . . . ."

This sentence jumped off the page at me. There was that word again! Karl and I were scheduled to attend a seminar in New Mexico right after Christmas. The name of the seminar? *Warrior's Wisdom.* We had been planning this excursion for quite a while, making reservations to get out to New Mexico at least ten months in advance.

I had not told Catherine of our plans, nor had I volunteered details of our trip to any of our friends. Indeed, our respect for Catherine and her powers of clairvoyance had been raised even more at the gathering in November when, the day before we found the owl, she commented to me (while channeling her guide and doing brief readings for all the participants in the room) that I would soon be starting to travel much more and would be moving into an expression of 'warrior energy.' For almost a year, Karl and I had played it all quite close to the vest, letting it be known only that we were going to New Mexico. There was no way Catherine could have known through 'regular' channels the kind of adventure Karl and I had planned.

So when I saw that Rabbit *used to be* a brave and fearless warrior, I immediately sensed that a message really was being sent to me and that I had better pay attention. It all just clicked into place for me. I saw, quite clearly, how I was allowing fear to rob me of my personal power.

I'm in the process of becoming a warrior, I thought to myself several minutes later, as I poked with a wooden spoon at the onion slices sauteing in the skillet. *My owl was a warrior and it got tripped up and died. It died carrying a rabbit. It died carrying fear.*

It died carrying dinner, my Ego remarked sarcastically.

As I started slicing zucchinis into the skillet, my mind kept going back to this new connection between warriors, fear, and death. I glanced at the wall clock to the right of our kitchen door. Karl would be home any minute. I couldn't wait to see what his take would be on all this. Did these things really have significance to me and my life? Did the Owl and the Rabbit have any true connection to our efforts to become spiritual warriors and the awful feelings of lack and fear and failure I'd been feeling lately? On the one hand it all seemed so obvious. But on the other, it seemed totally far out and far-fetched.

I'm no warrior, I caught myself thinking; *this is stupid.* I corrected myself. "I *am* in the process of becoming a warrior," I said out loud, just as Karl shoved the door open with his briefcase, "and I can't let fear keep screwing me up." I resolved to start watching my thoughts more closely.

"What?" Karl asked, smiling broadly at me as he held the storm door open for our stub-tailed cat to dart into the warm kitchen. "Mmmm, smells good," he said before I had a chance to answer.

CHAPTER FIVE

Christmas came and went, and before we could catch our collective breath we were in New Mexico. How exciting! Karl and I had never traveled together anywhere beyond the East Coast prior to this trip. We knew we had taken a leap of faith in deciding to attend the Warrior's Wisdom seminar. Although we had read Stuart Wilde's books, we still had no idea what to expect at this week-long 'intensive.' We knew of no one who had been to one of his seminars before, so we didn't have anyone we could press for details ahead of time.

Maybe it was just our own excitement—or the change in altitude—but as soon as we got off the plane in Albuquerque we noticed a shift in our energy. We felt clear and focused, ready for fun, adventure and growth. Walking through the airport, looking at all the great advertisements for the surrounding cultural and skiing attractions, we flirted with the idea of just bagging the course and going wherever our whims might lead us. It was a temptation! Despite our fleeting hesitation, though, we knew we'd come to this seminar for a reason. We were ready to grow—even if we were a bit scared of going through with it.

Within an hour we were driving up Route 25, out of Albuquerque and toward Santa Fe, in our newly rented Geo Prizm. The weather was absolutely clear, letting us see hundreds of miles in every direction. But the land before us, much to our surprise, was stark. Barren. Brown. Especially in contrast with the cobalt blue sky. This Southwest wintertime was a shock to our East Coast expectations of evergreens and snow.

"Hard not to put too many expectations on this trip, isn't it?" asked Karl, sensing from my sudden quietness that I was trying to keep myself from becoming too excited. "If we do that to ourselves, and the seminar itself, we'll regret it. I just know it."

"Yeah, but how do we stop them? I know—use discipline; allow no expectations." I shrugged my shoulders, answering my own question. Cocking my head toward the window, I added, "This landscape sure is enough to beat the crap out of any high expectations, isn't it?"

"What did we get ourselves into?" we sighed almost in unison. The images we'd had in our heads, created from the descriptions we'd read about Taos (our ultimate destination) as well as the photos so beautifully displayed in the airport, were a mocking contrast to the scenery before us.

We drove onward, trusting the instincts that had led us this far, and figuring that there was no turning back now just because the countryside was ugly. As we passed through Santa Fe and proceeded Northeast on Route 68, the brown dirt and clumps of sagebrush gave way to mountains and snow and the thrill of seeing the Rio Grande for the first time. To be honest, we were a bit shocked at how such a small body of water (really only a large creek by our Pennsylvania standards) could actually be termed the 'Great River.' But still, we began to get back into the swing of our adventure when our little car started climbing the mountains ringing Taos.

Soon we found ourselves traveling on a snowpacked surface, our wheels making that wonderful squeaky, scrunchy sound reverberate throughout the interior of the car. Great, towering piles of plowed snow stood guard beside the road, a testament to the transformation of our surroundings.

"This is more like it!" I exclaimed, my heart opening to the beauty unfolding before us. Karl agreed, his eyes gently taking in the grandeur of the scenery.

By the time we crested the mountain directly to the south of the town of Taos, the sun had set and the clear skies we'd seen in Albuquerque and Santa Fe had given way to a thick overcast which was starting to produce a mixture of snow and ice. The change was dramatic.

"Do you suppose we'll change this much in such a short time too?" Karl asked, sounding as though he half hoped for a 'yes' and half hoped for a 'no, of course not,' in response.

"I guess we'll get out of it what we put into it," I said. "I feel like this is going to open us up to new possibilities, but I'm afraid to get my hopes up. I don't want to be disappointed."

"I know how you feel," Karl agreed. "I don't either."

"All I know is, this is our last chance to bail out. We don't have to go to this thing you know," I said seriously. Suddenly, things were getting tight in the close confines of our car. Both of us shifted in discomfort, lost in the jabbering silence of our own thoughts.

The range of our emotions since landing in Albuquerque was astonishing. Up and then down. Steady . . . detached . . . then up into excitement and energy again. Quivering in anticipation for several minutes, we would suddenly find ourselves plummeting again, only this time hitting a new low. We had decided to participate in this seminar because we both felt a need to 'push the envelope' of our own personal growth. But now that we were here . . .

"I feel like I want to bolt," Karl said suddenly, making me jump. "But at the same time I can't wait to get to Taos and have this thing begin."

"I know! I feel the same way!" I agreed. "I think it's our egos' natural fear of change and 'not being in control'. All we need to remember is that we can always leave if we don't feel right about anything we're asked to do."

"Yup. And since we're in this together, we've got to be open and honest with each other if either one of us feels anything strange." He looked at me expectantly.

Taking my eyes off the road for a moment, our eyes locked. "Absolutely. We're that way with each other anyway, so why would we change now?" But I wasn't feeling as assured as I sounded. I was starting to feel spooked by everything.

It was as if our fears were specters, standing in the middle of the snow-covered road, blocking our passage. We had to drive through them, over them, around them, to get to our destination.

Here we were, two upstanding, college-educated professionals, married for ten years, with two children. *What the hell are we doing*, we asked ourselves, *flying for eight hours and then driving for another three, to the middle of nowhere, to participate in God-knows-what-kind of a wacky spiritual 'intensive'?! We don't even know what kinds of things we'll be participating in! What if something happens to us? Are we being IRRESPONSIBLE? Are we TAKING UNNECESSARY RISKS? Are we being IMPETUOUS? Are we doing something that 'normal' people wouldn't be caught dead doing?*

All of these fears and questions loomed up ahead of us as we entered Taos. We voiced them to each other, we mulled them over, and we argued their relative merits. We gave them some power for a minute or so, then together, we decided to ditch them, drive right over them. Finally pulling into our Inn's parking lot, we both expressed an audible sigh of relief.

"God, did we just run the gauntlet or what?" asked Karl with a grin.

"Mmm," was all I could muster as I wondered silently just what was in store for us on this 'vacation.'

CHAPTER SIX

The moment we entered the meeting room on the first day of the seminar, we found ourselves literally running a gauntlet; a gauntlet of eight expressionless people, four on either side of us, their faces illuminated with little but the light of the three fires burning in the large stone hearths within the room. Our greeters allowed no eye contact, and my attempts to find a smiling face to ease my sudden discomfort were unsuccessful.

A sweet smelling smoke was curling around the heads of the people already in the room and I felt myself stiffen inside when the haze greeted my nose and eyes. One of the flues is blocked, I thought to myself as I walked slowly, hesitantly, into the dimly lit room. I sensed that there was nothing to fear, yet my mind was screaming. Ahead of me, I saw a few members of the staff holding large bundles of obviously smoldering weeds. As I watched, they gently waved the smoky wands around each other and then around each person entering the room. Silently, imperatively, each participant was beckoned to walk through the smoke to the 'other side,' where the chairs had been arranged in auditorium style to face a raised dais. As haunting Celtic music swirled and echoed off the walls, we were curtly instructed to find a seat and admonished to maintain complete silence.

This was strange. Weird. An odd way to begin a seminar, for sure. I knew the weeds were not pot, but I didn't know what they were. I liked the smell, although my ignorance made me uncomfortable. It wasn't until later that night, when we were given a brief talk by a Metis (mixed blood) teacher named Hawk, that it dawned on me that we were being 'smudged' each time we entered the room.

This realization clicked a lot of things into place for me. I'd read Lynn Andrews' first book, "Medicine Woman," a month or so before and had brought her second book with me on the trip. I remembered in "Medicine Woman," Lynn describes the act of 'smudging,' which is a sacred method of cleansing and purifying the energy surrounding objects, people, and places, through the use of the smoke of burning herbs, usually sage. Until today, I had always envisioned a 'smudge' mark on the object being purified, similar to the smudge of ashes that is left by a priest on a person's forehead when blessed on Ash Wednesday. Experiencing the ritual of smudging for myself now cleared up my obvious misunderstanding. Each dawn, I began to welcome the sense of sacredness that this act of purification imparted to all our activities.

The first order of business was splitting our large group into smaller groups of 10 to 12 people. Stuart called these groups 'arbans,' a term he borrowed from ancient Mongolians. These were the people with whom we would be spending most of our waking hours during this week. Karl and I were in different groups, a fact we didn't like, but accepted as part of the experience. The first few days we attended lectures by Stuart, which were always entertaining, and participated in exercises geared toward learning to trust ourselves and our arban-mates. So far, I thought, this is fun—but not earth-shattering.

On the morning of the third day of the seminar, when we met for our first lecture of the day, rumors were flying around the room about what we were going to be doing that evening. When the rumors were confirmed by Stuart himself, I panicked. Suddenly, I was being faced with precisely the type of challenge to my understanding of reality that I had hoped to experience when we first decided to come to New Mexico. But this was also exactly what my ego feared most. To successfully negotiate this experience I was going to have to let go of a deeply rooted belief that is shared by almost everyone in the world: *fire burns*. Not only that, but for this to have deep, personal meaning to me, I must dedicate the act itself to my growth.

Stuart had said in his lecture that morning that one form of dedication is the active and deliberate relinquishment of something held dear to a person. Our beliefs about 'the way things are' are actually some of the most cherished possessions we have as human beings. They define who we are. In creating that definition they also, often without our realizing it, create boundaries which we dare not cross . . . or else. Or else what? Or else we won't be who we thought we were, which is a most frightening and threatening thought to our egos.

Therefore, in an effort to make this exercise more than simply an act of 'mind over matter' I needed to offer up, or sacrifice, a belief I was holding within myself that was keeping me from expanding spiritually.

Luckily for me, at the first break of the morning, I wandered over to the tables which had been set up in the back of our meeting room since the first day of the seminar. These tables were conveniently stocked with various books and tapes that we might want to purchase during our 'intensive.' With palpable relief I found that someone had recognized that some of us, upon discovering what we were going to be asked to do that night, would want to 'read all about it' before 'doing it' ourselves.

I'm a great one for reading all about 'it,' no matter what that 'it' happens to be. I take incredible comfort in books and words. The problem, at least for me, is that I sometimes allow *reading* about 'it' to substitute for actually *experiencing* 'it' myself.

Half wondering when in God's name I'd have a chance to read an entire book on the subject in the next ten hours, yet steadfastly ignoring that logical thought, I made my purchase.

Just holding it in my hands gave me a peace of mind that at the very least kept me from bolting from the room—and the seminar.

As soon as we returned to our seats after the break my mind kicked into high gear: OK. Do I worry about the experience itself and the enormity of overcoming the cultural—and simply human—belief that fire burns? Or do I dedicate most of my day to ferreting out the juiciest personal 'limiting' idea I have in order to 'sacrifice' it this evening? I struggled to listen to Stuart's lecture, the content of which addressed the same terrors, limitations, and disbelief as were scurrying around in my own mind.

"What belief are you going to give up tonight?" I asked Karl anxiously. We'd just completed the late morning lecture and returned to our room. The afternoon was ours to spend in preparation for the evening's 'festivities.'

"I think I'll sacrifice worry," Karl responded, his dark brown eyebrows furrowed in thought. "I haven't made up my specific list yet, but that seems to be something that I run into a lot with myself. What about you?"

"I don't know yet, I have to think about it," I snapped, surprised at the unexpected edge to my voice. "I'm not even sure I want to go through with this. I mean, after all, what if something goes wrong?"

"What if it does?" Karl asked pragmatically. "The worst thing would be that you'd get burned and need to be taken to the hospital. I'm not saying that would be good," he added quickly, "but I don't think you'd die. The experience of getting burned would obviously be a lesson in itself."

I could feel a tremendous sinking feeling in my stomach, and by the look in Karl's eyes I suspected that the feeling was reflected on my face.

"But I'm sure that won't happen," Karl said reassuringly. "Unless, of course, you're determined to make it happen."

"Oh right, like anyone in their right mind would choose to hurt themselves," I replied sarcastically.

"Well that's just it, isn't it?" Karl agreed. "If you go into tonight's challenge feeling out of balance or weak or profoundly doubtful of your abilities, then you really aren't in your right mind, are you?"

Sometimes he simply amazed me. I looked at him, momentarily unable to speak. "No, I suppose not," I paused, chewing on the inner flesh of my bottom lip. "Yuck!" I exclaimed, throwing myself onto the middle of the double bed, making the headboard bang loudly against the wall. "I guess that means that I have to decide whether or not I truly believe in our capacity, as humans, to withstand more than we are led to believe," I pontificated. It sounded good to me.

"No, Lis," Karl cut me off with the hint of a smile. "It really has nothing to do with other human beings at all. On a personal level, right down where it's just you and no one else, you have to decide how far you're willing to believe in yourself."

Karl's travel alarm clock ticked noisily on the nightstand as I realized I'd been busted.

"Aren't you *afraid*?" I blurted out, recognizing that the flip my stomach had just performed was an introduction to Fear 101.

"Not really," Karl replied matter-of-factly. "For some reason I know that I'll do it without a problem." He paused, as though deciding whether to continue. "I almost feel as though I've done it before."

It was maddening. He was so sure of himself that it made me want to scream. But he wasn't being arrogant, which made it oddly even worse. If he had been at all haughty I could have easily written his calm certainty off to ignorant machismo. What he really was doing, though, was allowing me no place to hide.

"Hmmmph," was all that I could come up with as I picked distractedly at a sharp edge on my left thumbnail. All of a sudden, I realized that I'd discovered, or rather uncovered, what I needed to sacrifice. How could I have missed it? It was just as I had feared.

CHAPTER SEVEN

Sitting up, I retrieved my journal from the bedside table and opened it to the last page, which was blank. Ripping it out, I nestled on top of the covers with a pillow tucked under my crossed legs. The other pillow was wedged between my back and the headboard.

"FEAR," I wrote firmly at the top of the page with my favorite purple pen. I underlined it twice just for emphasis in my own mind. On the first line I got more specific. "Fear of failure. Fear of failing myself. Fear of failing Karl. Fear of failing Daniel and Maximus."

I'm on a roll, I thought to myself as the lines of my spiral notebook paper quickly filled. I had never realized how truly fear-full I was until that moment.

Not wanting to lose the momentum, I continued filling the paper with my demons. "Fear of failing my mother and father. Fear of failing my clients. Fear of not being as good a lawyer as I think I should be. Fear of not making enough money. Fear of not working hard enough."

Wow! Where were all these fears coming from? And this failure bit. I didn't understand it. I didn't have a history of letting people down. So why was it such a great fear? I could even see that my anxiety about getting burned tonight, crossing a bed of hot coals in bare feet, was actually a fear of failing the seminar.

After filling over half the page with statements of specific fears that I was determined to release, I threw in a couple of other things that I'd been hanging on to, such as anger at certain people who had taken from me either monetarily or emotionally (and sometimes both ways). I didn't want those hurts to hold me back any longer, either.

Looking up from my paper and once again regaining aware-ness of our room, I noticed Karl working intently upon his list as well. I was surprised that he, too, was still writing and fleshing out his sacrifice.

"There really is something to the concept of making our ac-tions sacred, isn't there?" Karl said, looking up at me. It was as if he'd suddenly became self-conscious of how engrossed he'd been in his task. "I thought this would be a snap. Nothing to it!" he grinned. "But the more care I put into defining exactly what I want to release the more I see how limiting some of my thoughts actually are."

"I know," I agreed, nodding my head in disbelief as I looked at the sheet of paper I'd filled. "I started out with one word at the top of my list and now it's grown to at least 20 lines of specific areas in my life where that one concept, fear, has profoundly influenced my day-to-day thoughts and actions."

"If you hadn't gotten so absorbed in what you were doing I know I wouldn't have put as much time into this," Karl admitted. "I really thought I knew my limiting beliefs. In fact," he laughed, "when I first thought about it, I didn't feel limited at all! But when you put me on the spot like that, I thought I better sacrifice something. So I figured a nice generic thing like 'my worries' would be enough."

I just looked at him, taking some comfort in the fact that he seemed to be finding this process a bit unsettling too.

"I guess maybe I was glossing over some pretty important stuff though, now that I look at my list," he continued, his voice trailing off into the silence. "Geez, I'm shocked at the things I stress-out about!" Again, I didn't respond.

Finally, after a long afternoon of quiet and reflection, darkness blanketed our room. It was time to join the others. Carefully folding my list in half, and half again, and then a third fold for good measure, I tucked it into my pants pocket. Feeling lighter and less fearful than when I'd begun this exercise, I knew I was ready. And so was Karl.

CHAPTER EIGHT

Standing in a huge circle around two parallel beds of red hot coals, we held hands and said a prayer. We dedicated our ceremony to freedom, to releasing ourselves from those unique, personal, beliefs that kept each of us from living our lives to the fullest.

The night sky above us was a dark indigo and exquisitely clear. Huge clusters of gleaming stars seemed to have congregated above our heads to bear witness to our sacred ritual, their twinkling faces beaming silent support and encouragement. A solitary drum beat a calming, ancient cadence.

The freezing air seemed to crackle with unspoken conversation. Giddiness, wild anticipation, excitement, terror, all of these emotions were coursing through the air as vivid as moving pictures. Each breath that was exhaled seemed to crystallize as it passed our lips. We were in this together, focussed, determined, yet in truth knowing that this was something that each of us had to accomplish alone, for oneself.

At opposite ends of the courtyard, Karl and I weren't even going to share the same bed of coals. My stomach, already clenched in apprehension, knotted even tighter with disappointment. As the luck of the draw had it, he was to go before me. *Is that better or worse?* my mind screeched. Oh, God, I can't think!

I said to myself, trying to shush the doubts and fears and quell the rising panic.

I watched Karl, every cell in my body on alert, ready to run to him should he falter or even wince. I watched him deliberately bend down at the leading edge of the bed of coals to burn his list and release it to the Universe. Without hesitation, without missing a beat, my husband straightened his tall frame and, barefoot, walked boldly forward across 15 feet of searing heat, into the waiting arms of his arban members. Of course, he emerged from the fire unhurt, whole, and smiling, as he knew he would.

Steadily, one by one, sometimes two by two, people crossed. The illogical, the unexplainable, the seemingly impossible, kept occurring before my eyes, one person after another. My fingers, dug down deep into the pockets of my jeans, kept creasing and uncreasing my List of Fear. Reciting my fears verbatim, my ego was screaming at me to get the hell out of there. *You're CRAZY! What would your parents think if they knew what you were doing at this moment? Would you want your kids to be taking asinine risks like this? What kind of an example are you? You can't do this! I won't let you! I'll make you stop right in the middle of the coals and let you roast! I'll show you for the fool you are. No, I'll make you an injured fool. Yeah, that's it! I'll embarrass you. I'll embarrass Karl. I'll make him wish he wasn't with you. You're not strong enough. You can't shut me up long enough to make it across. NO WAY! There's NO WAY you'll do this! You're going to FAIL!*

"OK, I'm scared shitless!" I blurted out loud, slightly under my breath. A nervous laugh also escaped, but I felt precariously close to throwing up. The purity and spontaneity, though, of that simple admission caught my attention and made me realize what absolute insanity was chittering from my ego.

There was absolutely no pressure to take the walk, other than my own desire. I could turn away; leave. I could simply burn my list. Or I could do it all. It was my choice. My fingers kept rubbing the edges of the folded square tucked inside my pocket, wearing them down. *How important is it, Lisa, to release the be-*

liefs on this paper? I asked myself. *Are you ready? Is it time? Fear is standing here, right beside you. Will it escort you as YOU make this decision or will you allow it to lead you along the path IT wants you to take? You know, the path that says that fire burns and so does skin?*

I was there. Fully and completely within the moment, I watched for an eternity as I offered up my List of Fear and touched it to the coals in front of my bare feet. Instantly, it burst into flames and was gone. And with it, all hesitancy, all lingering doubt that this was, truly, a sacred moment, a turning point in my own empowerment.

Just before stepping onto the searingly hot coals, I remember asking Fear to stand beside me and keep me safe, but to NEVER again stand in front of me or keep me from doing and being the things I came here to do and be.

CHAPTER NINE

J oy, celebration, relief, and belief were some of the many emotions coursing through the freezing air. As each member of our group walked boldly, if briskly, across the glowing bed of red hot coals that night, he or she ultimately was greeted by the loving and welcoming arms of those who'd gone before. Each successful passage was yet another boost to our collective gathering of personal power and confidence. As each of us claimed our power individually, the whole arban—indeed, the entire group of seminar participants—tangibly benefited. Exclamations of love and pride and accomplishment pulsed through the night air. Some of our compatriots, perhaps disbelieving that they'd done it once, deliberately—and safely—made 'the walk' a second time.

After our celebration wound down and Karl and I returned to our room, I had a hard time quieting my thoughts enough to sleep. The ritual we'd just experienced had moved me in ways I could hardly express in my journal, although I tried.

Finding myself at a loss for words, my fingers gently caressed a small blister on the arch of my right foot just above my heel. The patch was about the size of a dime. Not a big, disgusting, oozing blister, it was actually just some redness with the hint of some fluid collecting underneath.

"Did you get burned at all?" I asked Karl, nudging him out of his light slumber as he lay cuddled up beside me under the covers. We'd been back in our room for maybe half an hour, tops. I couldn't believe he was actually sleepy after such a phenomenal event! Well, yes, I could believe it. It certainly wasn't out of character for him. He always seemed to be able to fall asleep anywhere after doing practically anything. Being a night person, this tends to drive me buggy, although I'd come to accept it over the years—for the most part. But there are times when I simply can't keep myself from inflicting my nighttime chattiness on him— and this was certainly one of those times!

"Come on, Karl, talk to me!" I cajoled, turning my full attention to the lump beside me that was my husband. "Here we are in Taos, New Mexico; we just walked barefoot across 15 feet of red hot coals not two hours ago, and you're actually falling asleep!" I struggled to keep the exasperation from my voice. "Now tell me," I demanded, my hand gently squeezing his left shoulder. "Did you burn yourself at all?"

Karl rolled over and sat up in bed. Wrapping his arms around his knees and giving me a look that said I better appreciate how much he loves me, he finally responded. "No. I don't have a mark on me."

"Are you sure?" I persisted, not believing that size 13 feet could actually make it through such a journey completely unscathed. I rooted under the covers and pulled his legs and feet on top of the comforter, pointedly ignoring his protestations, so I could look for myself.

I went over both his feet and his ankles and, sure enough, couldn't find the first hint of evidence that he'd just walked on fire.

"What about you?" he asked grudgingly, knowing that I'd started this conversation for a reason.

I showed him my little blister, which was starting to send out typical, sharp, burn-type pain signals. As he murmured some appropriately consoling remark, I began to notice the strangest emotion starting to surface. I was actually glad that I had this physical reminder of what I'd just experienced! It was almost like a trophy, although I knew it wasn't something I would take home with me, since it was, thankfully, such a superficial burn. But the simple fact of its presence gave me the opportunity to persuade my logical self (which had stormed back to our room that evening after failing to talk me out of participating in such crazy behavior) that I really had walked on fire.

"You needed to bring back proof of your walk, didn't you?" asked Karl with a teasing edge to his voice, obviously sensing the truth of the matter. "You think your ego isn't that intense, but boy! When your experience starts treading on hallowed ground—beliefs that you've held for as long as you can remember—it makes you pay for it!" He laughed, shaking his head.

He was right. I tend to tease Karl a lot about the apparent tenacity of his ego, implying, I suppose, that I don't have such intense internal battles. He was relishing this chance to point out the limits of my belief system, the places where my logical mind refuses to venture.

Knowing the power of my ego, my inner self had arranged for me to bring back to the room a small token of believability for my ego to chew on. *Can't deny THIS!* crowed my Higher Self.

No, you're right, sighed my ego, silently. *And because of that, it's time for bed. Maybe by morning the burn will be gone, or at least a logical explanation will have occurred to me by then.*

Giving Karl his due, I reluctantly closed my journal and placed it on the floor beside the bed. The magic of this night was dancing through me and I didn't want it to end. The range of emotions I'd experienced throughout this day had exhausted me. Yet I couldn't help but feel like some huge shift had taken place within me and I wanted to revel in the freedom I suddenly felt in my heart. I knew with a profound certainty as I lay there in the dark that somehow this experience had changed me in ways I didn't even comprehend. I felt different, but my mind simply couldn't define in a neat little category just what had been transformed by the fire.

Thanking the Universe for such a wonder-filled experience, I drifted off into a sound sleep.

CHAPTER TEN

Karl's alarm started chirping before even a hint of morning light began edging its way toward the horizon. He was up and out of bed, putting his contacts in and otherwise tending to his dawn ritual, as I lay in my usual early morning position, hovering half-way between consciousness and dreamtime, only my eyes and nose exposed to the cold air, the rest of me snuggled under the covers.

"Can you believe this is our last day?" Karl called to me from the bathroom as he turned the warm water on to rinse his razor.

"No," I groaned. "I don't want it to be all over!" A wave of sadness washed over me. Our time here at the Inn had gone by so quickly it seemed; yet maybe 'time' wasn't the appropriate yardstick in this case.

"Well, it isn't over yet, Lis," Karl responded. "We still have what might be the biggest day of all to experience."

"True enough," I mumbled, as I rolled out from under the blankets. I immediately set myself to the task of dressing for the day. I'd heard we were going to spend it in Carson National Forest, where a good 40 inches of snow covered the ground. On went thermal underwear (tops, bottoms and even thermal undersocks), a thermal sweatshirt and thermal sweat pants, wool socks, ski pants and my ski jacket.

Within a few minutes we were walking over packed snow that squeaked in protest to the bitter pre-dawn cold, making our way to the Inn's dining room across the courtyard from our room. We kissed goodbye at the door, having each made arrangements to spend this last morning with our arban-mates. I saw David, the 'leader' of our arban, as soon as I walked in the door. Giving Karl's hand one last squeeze, I made my way over to David's table and sat down.

"Happy New Year's Eve Day!" I said in greeting to my friends as I turned my coffee cup right side up in eager anticipation of it being filled by the waitress at my side.

"That's right!" "Good morning!" and "Oh, I'd forgotten that this was the last day of the year!" were the assorted comments that I heard from around the table.

Eating our breakfast of eggs, toast, hashbrowns, coffee and juice, we laughed and talked easily among ourselves, even beginning to reminisce a bit about the past few days although the experience was, in reality, far from over for any of us.

"I'm not worried about today," said Sally, a bright, petite woman in her early 40's. She'd been friendly enough throughout the seminar, although her focus had clearly been more on developing male interest than in cultivating kindred-spirit (gender neutral) relationships. "I don't find physical challenges nearly as tough as mental or emotional ones," she added.

I was surprised at her candor.

"I don't think today will be focused primarily on physical challenges, Sally," replied David. A tall guy with a quick smile and easy nature, I knew he'd recently been through a tough divorce and was considering moving to the United States from his native Saskatchewan. His life was in the course of realizing some major changes and he'd told me that he'd thought long and hard before making the commitment to come to this seminar. We'd chosen him as our 'leader' probably for his ability to relate to each of us individually, even though we were a fairly diverse group.

"Isn't this going to be some kind of a 'ropes course?'" asked Bill, who had arrived on the first day of the seminar with Sally. At first, they'd given the impression that they were here as a couple, but it now seemed like they were each on the verge of leaving this experience alone, separated. "Sounds pretty physically intensive to me!" he joked.

"No, really," persisted David. "If you think about it, what are the chances that a seminar like this one would end with simply a physical challenge for us to tackle?"

"I agree with David," I broke in, seeing that his point made sense. "Since we'll be dealing with high trees and other things that we're not even sure of, it's a safe bet that the real tests, besides being physical ones for some of us, will also be psychological. After all, 'leaping into the void' isn't so much a physical challenge as a spiritual or psychological one."

"All I know is that this has been the most fun I've had in years," commented Jacob in his deep, gravelly voice. Jake, also from Canada, was the oldest member of our group, in his late fifties or early sixties was my guess, and had been in business for himself for many years. Throughout the past five days, he had given me the consistent impression of being the 'strong, silent type.' Very stoic in nature, resilient; a man of few words—but, when ultimately spoken, those words revealed a kind and gentle being. Maybe because of some unconscious stereotype I have in my head about big, broad, Canadian men from the wild west (especially those who wear red and black checkered flannel shirts like Jake's), I associated Jacob with the image of a lumberjack.

His comment generated a round of agreement from all of us as to the fun we'd had so far. There was no use speculating about what the day had in store for us. We would discover our challenge soon enough.

Looking up from our table, I noticed that the dining room was starting to clear out. Karl and his fellow arban-mates had already left to gather in the main lobby of the Inn, where a warm fire crackled in the huge walk-in fireplace. Draining my cup of coffee, I joined my friends as we walked to the Inn's entrance, where we'd been instructed to wait for the jeeps and vans that would take us into the forest. I also wanted to give Karl another hug before we left.

Deep in my heart I felt that today would be Karl's biggest challenge. Mine, I reasoned, had definitely been the firewalk, with its attendant preparatory mental and emotional gymnastics. Although he had been relatively unfazed by that whole process, I knew that Karl's fear of heights stood a very good chance of being called to the forefront today. He knew it, too. I could tell by the slightly pale cast to his face as I caught sight of him standing near the door to the men's room.

"Be careful, OK?" I said quietly into his left ear as I stood on my toes to put my arms around his neck.

"Yeah, you too, bunny," he replied, giving me a strong, lingering hug.

CHAPTER ELEVEN

Several vans and 4-wheel drive vehicles were sitting in a line outside the Inn, engines idling, headlights cutting sharp slices of illumination through the freezing air. We huddled together, stamping our feet to keep the blood flowing in our extremities, and received cursory instructions: Silence. We would meet again as a group on the top of the mountain.

Our faces slowly became discernible to each other as daylight crept up. It was freezing cold out, probably sub-zero. The merriment shared during breakfast was gone, subdued, and our eyes reflected a curious mixture of worry, excitement, fear, and exhilaration.

The ride up into the mountains and deep forest took almost an hour and was spent in silence, as instructed. Despite our physical proximity to each other, we were alone; alone with our thoughts as to what this final day of the seminar—and the year—had in store for us.

The last mile was treacherous and a ripple of discomfort moved through our group when we recognized, simultaneously, that walking might suddenly become part of the plan. The snow was deep and the engine strained as our Jeep's tires fought to gain a foothold on the piled powder. But the chains found purchase and we continued our climb, shortly pulling into a circular clearing of plowed pathway.

Seeing a lone path in the snow leading over a small ridge and down into a saucer-like depression at the base of a huge forested mountain, we trudged in pairs and single file to the clearing. The silence we maintained was easier to keep here, with Nature providing us with this magnificent cathedral.

Our coordinator of the day's activities, a man experienced in leading groups such as ours through the rigors of a ropes course, had us form a large circle roughly 100' in diameter. He stood in the center and explained in a half-shout that we'd be going from one 'station' to another throughout the day, our arbans each being assigned an experienced climber from his staff. After listening to his relatively brief pep talk we learned that our arban's first event was to be 'the perch.'

Following the barely discernible path being blazed by our guide, Stacy, we climbed another 200 yards or so up into the forest. We were probably at around 11,000 feet above sea level at this point, and I could feel the thinness of the air in my lungs. I heard one of the guys in front of me mumble that just getting to the event was a test in itself, and as we approached this unknown challenge I could feel all of us starting to wonder, again, what we'd gotten ourselves into.

Not knowing what to expect, I'd been nervous about just what a 'ropes course' would require of me, and I hoped I'd be able to handle whatever I was asked to do. My hopes of doing so ran screaming back down the mountain when we stopped in front of a dead tree that stretched its way up a good 50' into the air. Of course, given the steep slope we were on, the tree seemed to extend even higher than its simple measurement from the ground. A rope ladder went about half way up, the rest of the way apparently meant to be scaled by the use of 3" by 3" wooden blocks, which were strategically nailed into the bark to form footholds. A thin circle of plywood, no more than 12" in diameter, had been fastened at the pinnacle of the tree. It was obvious to all of us that we were expected to climb to the very top, stand on the plywood disc, and launch ourselves toward a trapeze which was suspended about six feet away from the tiny platform, directly over our—now gaping—mouths.

A stunned silence wrapped itself around our little group. "They don't really expect us to actually *perch* up there, do they?" Bill asked no one in particular.

"Well, there's just no way I'm going to try this ridiculous exercise," announced Jean authoritatively. "Nope. No way," she added, sounding as though she was engaged in an inner argument with herself.

"We can do it you guys!" piped up Sally with a cheerleading attitude. I wanted to gag. She seemed so damn sure of herself and her physical prowess. I had no doubt that she'd negotiate this event with ease and that her enthusiasm was genuine. But as I gazed rather hopelessly at the teeny platform topping that very high, possibly unstable, tree, I felt like some sort of uncoordinated blob. Every cell in my body proclaimed that there was about as much chance of my scaling that dead fir as there was of me suddenly becoming a prima ballerina.

I didn't say a word, fearing that if I opened my mouth everyone would know without question what an out-of-shape chicken I was.

Then my mind took a different tack. Suddenly, I could see that this was all a mind game, a trap staged artfully by the presenters to scare the hell out of all of us. We weren't really expected to make it to the top of the tree at all, I told myself. Just climb as high as you can, then jump. Much as I wanted to embrace this version of what was expected of us, I didn't dare voice it, either. I didn't want anyone to disagree with me or in any other manner burst my comfortable little bubble. I decided to just stand back and watch some of the others go first.

"Hey guys, don't worry," said Stacy, in a voice that almost, but not quite, had a tinge of teasing to it. "You'll be hooked up to full mountain climbing harnesses. I won't let you fall and hit the ground . . . too hard!" she continued, her eyes dancing.

"Honey, you won't have a chance to save my butt from this

event," interjected Susan, a strikingly beautiful—and unique—woman from L.A. "I am hereby exercising my right to choose, and I choose *not* to shinny up some tree just to try to swing from a stupid trapeze. Nuh-uh, no thank you," she said with finality, crossing her arms in front of her.

I let out a relieved sigh. I'd stick by Susan. She had the right idea.

But as Stacy explained what was expected of us (yes, we were actually supposed to bring ourselves to a standing position and jump from the disc with the intention of grabbing the trapeze), I could feel a resolve come over most of the group, myself included. We were game. Yeah, what the heck. Who really cared if we didn't make it up the whole way? The point was to try. The challenge was in stepping forward and saying, "I'm next."

First up was Bill. My heart went out to him. He knew how gung-ho Sally was about this exercise. We all did, for heaven's sake. At this very moment she was busily trying to talk Susan into seeing the challenge from a 'different perspective.' It was no wonder that Bill sucked it up and volunteered to go first. Nothing like some good old fashioned male pride to spur one on to biting the bullet.

Sally and Diane helped Stacy adjust the harnesses and straps about Bill's body and legs. The rest of us stood around, stamping a clearing in the snow, quietly sharing our angst about what the rest of the day held in store, if this first event was any indication of what we had to look forward to. We'd been given permission to break our silence, but our words were spare and to the point.

Without wasting any time, and amidst wholehearted cheering and rousing support from all of us on the ground, Bill climbed to the top of the tree. Grasping the plywood disc, he demonstrated just how wobbly that puppy was. Halfway into a kneeling position, he suddenly slipped and sailed through the air like an overgrown Peter Pan. We cheered. It didn't matter that he hadn't even come close to the trapeze. He'd done it. He'd broken the ice for all of us.

Surprisingly enough, given her adamant stance against the whole idea when we'd first arrived, Jean volunteered to go next. There was a determination in her voice that escaped no one. Much as she didn't want to participate in this exercise, it was obvious that she intended to give it her best shot. It was also obvious that she intended to get it over with as quickly as possible, now that she'd made the internal commitment to try it. "I need to go next," she declared as Bill extricated himself from the climbing gear. *Need* was the operative word here. We all heard it. We all respected it.

Collectively, we held our breath as Jean started her ascent. Climbing a rope ladder is no easy task for most people, but for Jean, who had a left hand comprised of only two fingers and a thumb, the climb seemed doubly difficult. Her courage and determination made me wince in embarrassment at my internal whining.

"Don't be surprised or upset if I have to let go pretty quickly," Jean warned out loud. "My hand has a tendency to cramp up when I try to do too much with it," she added, whipping off her mitten and, I suspect, somewhat enjoying the shock value her action had on the unsuspecting Stacy.

To her credit, Stacy recovered almost instantaneously, responding evenly, "Don't *you* worry about *me*. Keep the focus on the climb. No matter how far you get—or don't get—it will be safe for you to just let go."

"Alright, Jeannie, time to do it," Jean mumbled quietly to herself as she stepped up to the tree and grasped the rope ladder. Clasping onto the rope as best she could, she hauled herself up the first several 'rungs.' The rope swayed back and forth, making her progress slow and labored. Just as Jean reached the wooden blocks, which looked as though they would be easier to hang onto than the obviously hard to control rope ladder, she spat out a disgusted, "Forget it," and let go.

It seemed to me she'd gotten herself through probably the hardest part of the entire exercise, only to let go when she could have made real progress. But who was I to judge? At least she'd done it. I didn't see myself clamoring to be next in line.

Next up was Miss Enthusiasm, Sally. True to form, she climbed that pole like a sleek feline, with grace and agility. It was actually a pleasure to watch her scale the tree so fluidly, probably because it allowed me to fantasize that I'd be able to climb up easily as well. Although able to get to the top, crouch on the plywood and launch herself, Sally missed the trapeze. But she sure did make it look fun.

Diane was next. Her climb was not unlike her personality, gentle and unobtrusive. She approached the event with quiet determination, executed the task she'd set for herself, but like Sally, missed the trapeze! She showed only a little disappointment, and by the time she returned to earth, her face was glowing with accomplishment at having met the challenge.

Good old 'lumberjack Jake' followed Diane. As he negotiated the rope ladder and moved on to the wooden blocks, he made a wry comment as to how he 'should have quit smoking three months ago.' Talk about determination. It was oozing out of Jacob's pores.

Clearly, this was a man with a mission. As he approached the plywood disc at the top of the pole, we could tell that the climb was more of a strain than his cavalier comments would have us believe. He was wheezing and obviously needed to rest before attempting to balance himself on the tiny platform. Instead of just taking a breather, however, he very meticulously adjusted the disc with one hand, tightening it and making it far less wobbly for the remainder of us, while keeping a tight clutch on the pole with the other.

Slowly, carefully, Jacob managed to guide his bulky body onto the perch. It had been one thing to see two petite women negotiate their bodies onto that space, but it was quite another to see such a large man concentrate and balance all of his mass on such a small area. Once up, Jacob gazed away from our direction and focussed his sights toward the several mountains in the distance. While Bill, Sally and Diane had all made it to the top as well, their focus had been on accomplishing the next portion of the task, which was launching themselves toward the trapeze. Jacob, on the other hand, was clearly enraptured by the magnificent beauty revealed to him from his vantage point.

There was something special going on up there. Some connection was being made between Jacob and . . . the Universe? David, standing next to me, nudged my arm and whispered, "Do you see something different about Jake?"

Before I had a chance to answer, he added, "Wow! Do you see that?"

A reverent silence had come over every one of us, and we all stood there in the snow as Jacob, now kneeling on one knee, arms outstretched toward the mountains and trees in the distance and the blue sky overhead said, "So this is what it's all about."

There was no doubt about it. Jacob wasn't just talking about our event.

His aura was unmistakable. The man glowed with a bright, whitish-yellow light that emanated at least twelve inches from his body. I asked David if he'd been referring to Jake's aura, and David nodded. I whispered that I'd never been sure I was actually seeing an aura before this moment, and David admitted he felt the same way. We'd heard about them, and read about them, and thought we'd seen them faintly on other people before. But this—this was undeniable.

It felt as though Jacob stayed in that position for several minutes. It could have been years. It may have been seconds. Discussing it later, we all agreed that time had been suspended for all of us.

Stacy, knowing that we had a schedule to keep but clearly not wanting to abruptly disturb the magic, quietly suggested to Jacob that he set his sights on the trapeze.

Jacob didn't verbally acknowledge her comment, although he did turn toward the face of our mountain. His aura continued to blaze. His voice, seemingly choked by tears and unmistakably laden with emotion, called out, "Fear, be with me!" Then he cried out loud as he jumped like a giant bear toward the trapeze.

When he landed, about four people rushed to hug him and tell him how loved he was and what an inspiration his climb had been to all of us. There was much crying and laughing and hugging as the tension of Jake's climb was broken. Clearly this had been moving for us, but most of all for Jacob, I realized, as I heard him let out three ragged, deep-sounding sobs. Not wanting to interfere with his process, David and I stepped back to give the man his space.

A minute or so of hugging went on before those closest to him noticed that Jake wasn't assisting in their efforts to get him on his feet and out of his harnesses. As the well-wishers stepped back from him, everyone saw that Jake's face was blue. With sudden force, Jean yelled, "Cardiac arrest!"

CHAPTER TWELVE

J acob never regained consciousness.

The fact that he took that step, that final leap, crossing over to another dimension in the presence of his arban-mates, made me shiver. We'd been drawn together to witness Jacob's courage. Adamantly believing that 'everything happens for a reason,' I was still shaken and uneasy. I knew there was a message for me in this but I didn't want to receive it. Judging from their reactions, my friends felt the same way.

You're just being superstitious again, I berated myself. *You're so self-centered that you're actually translating this poor man's death into a message to YOU?!?!* My ego scoffed, ripping my intuition to shreds.

Yet I suddenly found it impossible to rid myself of images of my mother that kept popping into my mind; my mother—and the owl I'd found two months earlier. I felt sure that Jake's passing was opening the door to the other side, at least in my own consciousness, and I vainly kept trying to slam it shut again. I did not want to see or hear how these events were connected.

My mother's declining health had been an area of denial and self-delusion for me, my family, and my mother herself for at least five years. In recent months, however, it had been getting progressively harder both for Mommy to 'cover up' the extent of her symptoms and for the rest of us to continue the charade of 'not seeing' the signs. I ignored those fleeting grimaces of pain crossing her face, the decline in her appetite, the increasing frequency of her nosebleeds and the swelling of her abdomen. I pretended not to notice how her cheekbones were becoming too prominent and how it grew harder for her to focus her attention. I didn't want to believe that my mother was going to die in the year to come, yet that was the unwanted message I couldn't escape.

Only two hours had gone by since Jake's death. The paramedics, who met us at the circular clearing and immediately began life support attempts, had tried to give us the impression that he might survive. In fact, we would not receive 'official' verification of his death until later that night. But we knew. Every one of us who'd witnessed Jake's passing knew that his spirit had soared that morning—and chosen not to return. After watching the ambulance disappear down the snowpacked road, we met as an arban and discussed whether we should stay with the course as planned or stop in his honor. We decided that Jake would want us to continue.

Suddenly aware of my surroundings, I struggled. My stomach scrunched into a knot. We were at our next 'station' and I found myself—literally—walking across a high wire which had been strung from the side of the mountain and extended out across ground that fell steeply away. The other end of the wire had been fixed to a platform built into trees rising some 75 feet into the air. As I stood on one cable, I held onto another which had been strung parallel to and about six feet above the one on which I stood. To get to the platform I had to take steps on the bottom wire while sliding my hands, which were raised above my head, along the upper cable. I was halfway across, stuck, thinking over and over to myself, *I can't do this. I'm not strong enough. I can't do this. It's too much.* Exactly the same words I'd used while giving birth to both of my sons. Birth words. Death words.

As I resisted moving forward toward the platform, I swung

wildly. My arms stretched straight up as my fingers clung to the wire above me, while my knees, locked straight in terror, pushed my feet in the opposite direction. Since I was at the midpoint of this exercise, the 'play' in the wires themselves was at its greatest. I believed I could go no further, yet there was no turning back. My body was stretched to hyperextension between the parallel wires and I felt as though I'd lost all control over the muscles in my arms and legs. A deep, groaning wail came up from the depths of my belly.

"Lisa, trust your body! Let yourself get to the other side!" These words broke through my spastic fright and I looked down at the caring faces of David and Sam. My mates were there for me, some 30' below, coaxing me to unlock my rigid stance and move toward the platform.

"You can do it, Lisa, you know you can," called Sam. His sincerity penetrated my panic. I was momentarily astonished that it was Sam who was encouraging me. He'd spoken very little over these past days and had given me the impression of almost painful shyness. The fact that he would break his silence to give me a boost of courage acted like a wake-up call to me. Deep, deep down, I *did* know I could do this. I latched onto that primal knowing and moved my hands and feet, trusting myself. To my surprise, I found that the bigger, more confident steps actually felt less threatening than the tentative, fearful ones. The cables wobbled, my body stretched first forward, then back, but I refused to let go. I just kept moving. Quickly, I made it to the platform . From there, I rapelled the 75' to the ground without further incident or fanfare and landed in the welcoming arms of my surviving arban mates.

As the day wore on, the shock of Jake's death took over, and though we managed to complete the remaining stations, we weren't really present. We just went through the motions. I struggle to remember what we did or how we even got through it. But we did.

Pushing the key into the lock, I prayed that Karl would be in the room. I'd caught glimpses of him during the day from afar. I knew he had made it through the day intact. I just wanted to see him and hold him and have him hold me. But he wasn't there. I was alone.

Sighing, I decided to begin my New Year's Eve by stripping out of my thermal layers and letting hot water flow over the enormity of my day. Stepping out of the shower, I was relaxed enough to marvel at the billowing clouds of steam I'd created. I took a deep breath of the hot fog and held it, slowly counting to ten. A tickle caught in my chest and I blew out the air quickly, much more quickly than intended. I caught my breath and started coughing, choking on my own saliva, a sure sign of my exhaustion.

"You OK?" Karl asked, poking his head into the tiny bathroom. The steam billowed out into the room and Karl laughed. "What are you trying to do, pickle yourself?"

"I'm alright," I laughed sheepishly. "I think I was so mellow from that shower that even my throat muscles forgot how to do their job." Wrapping the towel around myself, I walked into the harsh, cold reality of our room. "I'm glad you're back," I said, kissing him deeply.

Stepping back from our embrace, I asked, "Did you hear about Jake?"

Karl closed his eyes, wincing. "Yeah, I did." He looked at me again, his eyes filled with compassion. "How awful. You guys must be so sad. I wonder about his family . . .?"

"I don't want to think about it right now," I said, gently cutting him off.

"You were in there a long time," Karl prodded, unzipping his pants to take a shower himself. I appreciated how easily he shifted the conversation. "If we want to get over to the party in time, we'd better start dressing." I didn't respond. I just kissed him again, glad we were alive.

Karl looked over my shoulder at the clock on the nightstand.

"I'm a quick dresser," he flirted, his eyes dancing. "What about you?"

It wasn't until later that evening, after the combination New Year's Eve/farewell party, that Karl and I had a chance to describe for each other our experiences of the day. It was only then that I began to see more clearly the similarities between my reaction to being stuck in midair on the high wires and the 'transition' phase of giving birth to my sons. Both required, for me, a relinquishment of 'control' and a surrender to instinct and my body's wisdom. As for Karl, the wave of exhilaration and adrenaline generated by the ropes course had carried him over his fear of heights, helping him negotiate the events with more focus and ease than either of us had expected.

"I had fun," Karl stated simply, after describing in detail the one event that had given him a 'goose.' "I think I kind of did an end run around my fears today when I saw that *falling* didn't mean I would crash full force into the ground," he confessed.

"Which part of the course taught you that?" I asked, silently amazed at the difference in our experiences of the day.

"At first, I wanted to do everything perfectly and was my typical rigid self," Karl continued, smiling at the way he knows he can be. "But at the second station we went to, everybody was falling off this huge log that was suspended in the air horizontally between two massive trees. Not one of us made it across. That event, though, helped me feel what it must be like to fly—and with the ropes all hooked up to me, I knew I was safe. So I just decided to enjoy it."

"That's neat," I said, rubbing my hand along his thigh and giving his leg a squeeze.

"What about you?" he asked, laying back on the comforter and pulling me down beside him. "I guess you guys didn't have much of a chance to do the course, what with Jake and everything," he asked tentatively.

"That certainly did change everything," I admitted. "I can't believe he's dead, Karl. We had breakfast together just this morning!" I shook my head, tears welling up. Karl reached over and held me in his arms, hugging and rocking me gently.

"But we did go on," I said, sitting up again. "We decided that Jake wouldn't have wanted us to stop, since there was nothing we could do to bring him back anyway." I shrugged, a little embarrassed at the fact that our world hadn't stopped—even when one of our own had died.

"So what did you end up doing, besides the perch?" Karl asked.

"I never ended up doing that," I said, wrinkling my nose. "Not that I minded missing it!" I laughed softly. "But after we got Jake into the ambulance, we decided to just continue with the rotation. That took us to the station where we walked across the parallel wires and finished by rappelling."

He nodded. "I remember that one. That wasn't so bad."

I rolled my eyes and launched into a description of how much trouble I'd had getting myself across the ravine.

After I finished, Karl looked at me a long time before pointedly asking me, "What are you giving birth to, Lis?"

His simple question took me by surprise and made me squirm with discomfort. I didn't know! Today I'd witnessed a man come face to face with the essence of life, obviously enraptured by the experience, and yet choose to die, at least to this physical plane of reality. I'd also experienced, with excruciating discomfort, the feelings I associate with giving birth. Life is a circle; everything is connected. I knew that. But there was a more personal undertone to these experiences. Was a part of me dying and another being born? On some level, I sensed that might be true, but I couldn't see it.

Frustrated and confused, I looked at Karl, tears spilling onto my cheeks. I had no answer for him—or myself.

CHAPTER THIRTEEN

The next morning dawned overcast, with a breath-stealing rawness to the air. The goodbyes among my arban mates were stilted and forced, our moods as dark and thick as the blanket of clouds above our heads. An uneasiness had settled about us that none of us dared to acknowledge or articulate. We'd shared an intimacy that few people ever do. In that moment in time that was but yesterday we'd seen each other's emotions stripped to their essence by Jacob's death, virtually in our arms.

While other arbans were enthusiastically exchanging addresses and telephone numbers, with promises to write and perhaps even visit each other, we were subdued. It was different for us—we'd had a death in the 'family' and were still in shock. In fact, Jake's passing probably signalled a death of an aspect of each one of us. We were, unlike the others, in mourning—for Jacob and for ourselves.

I know that there was a part of me that wanted to run from this experience. The firewalk, the self-reflection, the friendships, all were irreplaceable. But the ending—the death—was an aspect I simply did not want to face. And my arban mates were a stark reminder of that death. I was, therefore, fairly eager to have them step out of my life, and not especially keen on ever seeing them again; and I sensed that they, too, felt the same way. On that somewhat unsettling and lonely note, we bade each other farewell.

This was also the first day of the new year. Karl and I had decided to stay on in Taos an extra couple of days, so we left our inn to find some breakfast and see what might catch our fancy in town.

As we sat in a small bakery along highway 64, munching fresh-made doughnuts and sipping hot coffee, we overheard two women asking the baker for directions to Taos Pueblo. In celebration of the first day of the new year, they said, the men of the Pueblo perform a 'Turtle Dance,' and allow non-natives to view the ceremony.

"What do you think?" asked Karl, one eyebrow cocked questioningly as we listened in on the conversation. "Want to go?"

"Sounds perfect!" I responded enthusiastically. This was just the diversion I needed to cushion the impact of the last several days. Although we'd hoped to go skiing after the seminar, we'd agreed this morning that we were both too exhausted physically, mentally, and emotionally from the previous day's events to tackle the side of another mountain. The prospect of watching a Native ceremony to welcome the new year was much more our speed.

Following the directions we'd overheard in the bakery, we made our way through the town of Taos and onto the single road that leads to Taos Pueblo. Almost anywhere you go in this town it is impossible to lose sight of Taos Mountain and the other surrounding peaks of the Sangre de Cristo chain of the Rockies, but as we approached the Pueblo on the spartan, flat road, the immensity and grandeur of these mountains was absolutely breathtaking.

"I can't see the Pueblo yet, can you?" I asked Karl as I squinted through the windshield. "Maybe I should have stayed on Route 64 a little longer?"

"No, I think you took the right road, " Karl mumbled, seeming lost in thought.

"But *look*," I argued. "There's nothing but Taos Mountain ahead of us. Can you see any sign of a village?"

Just then we noticed a weathered sign. "Welcome to Taos Pueblo," it stated. "Registration booth ahead." We kept driving, even though we still couldn't see any evidence of a village ahead. After another mile of passing the occasional horse, standing as still as stone in the snow-covered meadows, with tendrils of steam puffing from their nostrils the only evidence of life, and Taos Mountain looming ever larger before us, we came upon Taos Pueblo.

We paid the small registration fee and received strict instructions that absolutely no pictures or videos were to be taken because of the sacred nature of the Turtle Dance ceremony.

"It feels as though we've stepped back in time," I said with relish as we got out of the car. "Did it seem to you like the Pueblo simply appeared out of nowhere as we got closer to the registration booth?"

"Yeah. Almost like Camelot," Karl agreed, turning himself slowly around to take in the sights and sounds of the Pueblo as a whole. The air felt different here than it had in town. The aroma of sopapillas, a fried, sweet-tasting bread often eaten with honey, or sugar and cinnamon sprinkled on top, lingered on the air.

We'd been instructed to park in a courtyard of sorts. A group of several adobe buildings of varying heights, mostly two or three stories high, stretched from behind us and to our left in an L-shaped configuration, and then extended straight out before us toward Taos Mountain. Many of the adobes were connected together, while a few were separated by narrow spaces wide enough to fit only one or two people astride. The orange-hued structures rose seamlessly from the ground, obviously constructed from the same earthen material as the stuff upon which they stood. Rough hewn wooden ladders of differing heights leaned against many outside walls, as well as from some lower roofs to their higher neighbors. Paneless windows were covered with brightly colored weavings or simply left bare.

Cold as it was, children chattered and squealed in delight as they climbed the ladders to the upper levels of the Pueblo, joining their mothers and friends for the best view of the ceremony.

"I wonder if Taos Mountain protects her native people by providing them with a cloak of invisibility?" I mused out loud, as we both stood still in the middle of the courtyard-turned-parking lot. "It looks and feels like the mountain is actually cradling the Pueblo to herself. Maybe that's why these people have been able to live here, generation after generation, for what—almost a thousand years?"

Before Karl could answer we were startled by a high pitched male voice calling out in a manner that made us both snap to attention. The cry, a melodious chant that cut the ice-cold air, was answered by several men and boys in unison. The cadence of drums and rattles suddenly filled the atmosphere. We ran to some high ground beside one of the adobes as a double line of men and boys, clad in costumes of feathers and brightly colored ceremonial clothing, danced in a procession in front of us. Most had leather ankle bracelets with bells attached, so their every move jingled in a festive celebration of the new year.

As the dancers performed, I looked around and noticed the rapt pride with which many of the women and smaller children were watching their husbands, sons, fathers, and brothers. It was obvious that participation in this event was a special privilege.

The dancers moved about the entire Pueblo, giving performances at three or four key parts of the village. As the procession crossed over a wooden plank footbridge spanning the creek that flows from sacred Taos Mountain, Karl and I drifted away from the trailing crowd of sightseers. We much preferred to drink in the vaguely familiar sights and sounds of life on the Pueblo without having to listen to the curious brashness with which so many of the tourists seemed to treat the people of the Pueblo. And as beautiful as the dance was, I couldn't shake the feeling that what we were seeing was only the surface of the ceremony; that experience had taught the Taos people to distill the deep, sacred nature of the celebration for public, non-Native, consumption. Considering the attitudes and comments we heard from some of the visitors, I could understand why.

Karl and I drifted slowly across the courtyard, deciding whether to look in the various shops that lined the plaza or to sample some 'Indian Tacos,' listening all the while to the continued chanting of the warriors across the creek. Suddenly I became aware of an Indian man, in his mid-forties or so, walking directly toward us from across the plaza. As the man, who I presumed was a resident, approached us, I felt a mixture of curiosity and un-ease. He appeared to be walking toward us with some deliberateness, which was unusual, because it seemed as though all the other natives in the Pueblo tried to avoid contact with the tourists except to sell them souvenirs or jewelry.

"Do you see this guy coming toward us?" I hastily whispered to Karl, half turning my body away from the approaching man.

"Yeah," Karl responded, glancing beyond my shoulder and flashing a big smile, obviously making eye contact with, and welcoming, the Indian as he closed the distance between us.

"Is he coming over here? To us?? Have we done something wrong?" I questioned Karl, my paranoia taking the lead over all the other, more excited, emotions I was feeling.

"I don't think we've done anything wrong, but I guess we'll find out. Why don't you turn around and be friendly?" Karl whispered back just as the man walked up to us.

The Indian man immediately smiled and started talking to us as though we were old friends. We chatted about the ceremony and he asked us whether we'd enjoyed the braves' performance. If he introduced himself, I totally missed his name in the midst of my discomfort over this surprising overture of friendliness. I felt like I was a fake somehow, that this man was mistaking us for someone else that he knew or had met before.

But the conversation didn't end there. "I was just elected last month to be a representative of my people on the governing council," he stated with some pride.

"That's great!" we exclaimed in unison. "You must feel very good about the confidence your people have in you," I continued enthusiastically.

"Well, not really," he replied, shaking his head. "I don't understand for sure why I was selected."

"Oh, come on," I cajoled. "I'm sure they must feel that you'll do a good job in representing them. Why else would they have elected you?"

"Well, you see," he began, looking down at the ground and shuffling his feet uncomfortably, "my father was on the council for years and years. He was head of it for awhile, even. I think that maybe they elected me because my father was such a good leader. I guess I'm afraid I'll disappoint them."

The fact that this man cared at all about whether or not he was capable of shouldering the responsibility of governing his people made me think that he would probably do a good job. But I didn't know him, I argued with myself. Yet I sensed a sincerity about him that made me feel he had integrity, and I said so.

"Maybe your people see something in you that even you don't recognize in yourself yet. If you do your best, that's all anyone can ask of you."

At this point, he began telling us about certain responsibilities that were expected of tribal leaders, including various meetings they had to attend, and decisions they had to make which affected the entire tribe. As I stood there listening to him, my mind was reeling. What in the world was going on here? Why was this native American standing here talking to us in such great detail about the responsibilities of being on the tribal council, when he didn't know us from Adam? The whole scenario felt surreal and somehow out of context.

As my mind wandered in puzzlement over this odd situation, I noticed that Karl was paying rapt attention to the conversation. I noticed myself feeling anxious, yet intrigued by it all. As I started to bring my attention back to the substance of the man's dissertation on the finer workings of Indian tribal affairs, he suddenly stopped speaking, mid-sentence, looked directly into my eyes and pointed his finger toward my heart.

"Know yourself," he stated solemnly.

"Pardon me?" I asked in uneasy surprise, suddenly feeling my blood race through my veins. My heart was beating rapidly and I seemed to hear a buzz in my ears as I looked directly back into his eyes.

"Know yourself," he repeated, steadily returning my gaze.

CHAPTER FOURTEEN

"Umm, sure. O.K.," I barked out with a stilted laugh. My mind, meanwhile, was screaming. *What the hell does that mean?! This guy's a kook! I've been trying to 'know' myself for the past damn week! Can't he tell that I've just undergone a transformation? Why would he come up and say that to me? It must be a mistake. No, a coincidence. He should have said this to me before I did the seminar, not after! Oh, forget it. This is all a bunch of bull.*

"Well, it was very nice talking to you," I said out loud, trying to politely dismiss this unwanted messenger. "I'm sure you'll do a great job on the council." Awkwardly, I thrust out my right hand in an effort to end the conversation NOW.

Smiling broadly, the Indian man returned my handshake with a strong, firm grip. "You really should come into my shop," he said teasingly, cocking his head to indicate a doorway across the courtyard. "I have some beautiful pieces."

"Yes. Well, I don't know," I stuttered, looking at Karl in a panic but trying not to show it.

Karl looked at me blankly.

I wanted to scream at him and smack him in the arm really hard. Why wasn't he helping me? Couldn't he see that I wanted to get out of here *right now*?

"Sure, why not?" Karl said, agreeably glancing from the Indian to me. We both enjoy browsing at handmade jewelry and I could tell Karl thought this was a special opportunity. He looked at me expectantly and I could tell that he was starting to feel confused about my reaction. Why wasn't I eagerly trotting over to peruse our new friend's wares?

Meanwhile, I felt exposed and raw. My mind was reeling and the buzz between my ears was growing louder and louder. I could hardly speak.

"I've got to get back to my place," the man said. I heard his voice as though he were at the far end of a long tunnel. "Maybe we'll meet again some day."

"Yes, maybe!" responded Karl enthusiastically. "Bye!"

"Goodbye," he said to both of us.

I stood there, mute.

After the Indian turned and started walking slowly toward his kiosk, Karl turned to me and asked impatiently, "What is your problem?! Why did you act so weird all of a sudden? And why don't you seem to want to go to his shop?" he demanded. Confusion and irritation laced both his voice and his gaze.

"Karl!" It was all I could do to get his one syllable name out of my mouth. I looked deeply into his eyes, silently begging him to recognize the complete chaos I was experiencing emotionally. "Didn't you hear what he said?"

"What?" Karl responded, his face expressionless.

"Didn't you hear him? Didn't you hear what he said when he pointed his finger at me?" I felt like I was shrieking but no one seemed to be looking in our direction.

Suddenly, I felt like I was going to throw up or break down into uncontrollable sobs. Was I crazy? Had I made it all up? What was wrong with me?

"You mean when he told you to know yourself?" Karl asked, a big smile on his face. "Yeah, I heard him say that."

Relief flooded into my consciousness, but the buzzing inside my head continued. I looked around me and everything seemed to ripple—as though I had opened my eyes under water. I felt like I was going to faint, but at once I was filled with an enormous wave of aggravation with Karl.

He looked at me, his eyes dancing. "That was neat, wasn't it?"

"Neat!" I snorted. "Neat? Didn't you think it was *weird?*" Buzzing. Nausea. *I've got to get out of here,* I thought.

"Well, gee. No. I didn't think it was all that weird," Karl answered somewhat defensively. "It seemed to kind of fit in with the whole reason we're out here to begin with."

"But Karl," I pleaded. "Didn't it strike you as odd the way he just came up to us and told us so much personal stuff about himself? And then, totally out of the blue and completely out of context, he tells me to *know myself?*"

"I guess so," Karl shrugged. I could tell he thought I was overreacting, but I didn't care. I had to get out of there.

"Let's go, " I said abruptly, changing the subject. "I feel really strange." I described the buzzing noise and the way my insides felt like they'd been somehow scrambled with an egg beater. "Maybe I'm just starting to feel the effects of yesterday," I said, Jake's image suddenly coming to mind.

"Probably," agreed Karl. "I don't have any great need to go to a bunch of shops." We started walking toward the car. "I think we got more out of our visit here than we expected anyway," he added, putting his arm around me and drawing me close.

When we reached the car I unlocked the driver's side door but, instead of opening it, I leaned against it, lifting my face to the warmth of the sun — which, I suddenly realized, hadn't emerged from the clouds until we'd started talking with the Indian!

"Are you OK?" Karl asked gently, starting to fully realize that I wasn't.

"I guess so," I lied, telling him what he wanted to hear.

We got in the car and slowly drove past the registration booth, retracing our path back toward town. I focussed on breathing deeply and tried to empty my mind of all thought about the Indian and his message.

As we passed a second long-furred horse, now peacefully munching a mouthful of hay and looking much warmer than it had when we'd arrived, I could contain myself no longer. "That really spooked me, Karl."

Karl sighed. "I can see that, Lis, and I don't know what to say."

"The whole situation just really threw me for a loop," I said, trying to make sense of my bizarre physical, mental, and emotional response to those two simple words: *know yourself.* "I think I thought I'd made so much progress this week that when he said that to me I felt like he must have made a mistake. But now," I said, shaking my head, " I feel like maybe I don't have a clue as to who I really am. And that really bums me out."

"I think you're making way too big a deal out of this," Karl said, shifting his position in the passenger seat so that his body was facing more in my direction.

"Right. It's extremely common for a Native American to approach a stranger visiting his Pueblo and tell her to know herself. Happens all the time!" I snapped.

I gently put my foot to the brake as I pulled up behind a tan Mercedes with Texas plates. We were several cars back in line at the stop sign marking the intersection with Route 64. The buzzing in my ears was much softer now, more like a very faint ringing. I was starting to feel somewhat more calm, more like 'myself,' but I wasn't ready to simply let the experience fade away into memory.

"It's not even what he said that really bothers me now," I said out loud, as I patiently waited for the cars in front of me to make their way onto the highway. Each one, after stopping, turned left heading back toward Taos. Without thinking, I turned right.

"What is it then, Lis? Obviously you're upset," Karl prodded gently.

"My reaction," I said simply. "As much as I want to believe that I know myself," our eyes briefly locked as I emphasized the word *believe*, "my reaction—my extreme agitation—shows me in no uncertain terms that I have a lot of work to do yet before I truly know myself."

"Hmmmph," Karl grunted, obviously not wanting to hazard a comment. After a long pause he asked, "Where are we going?"

"I don't know!" I laughed. "I guess I just didn't want to follow the crowd, so I turned this way."

"Story of our lives," Karl joked, half under his breath. "Let's go up to Taos Ski Valley and check out the slopes."

"OK!" I agreed. Suddenly, it seemed, the spell had broken. I tried my best to put the whole incident out of my mind. And it worked . . . for awhile.

CHAPTER FIFTEEN

With an almost audible thump, we found ourselves back in the 'real' world. Suddenly, we were right in the middle of the rat race, feeling no more in balance or enlightened than we had prior to our Taos adventure.

My first day back in the office was spent not only catching up on the messages and correspondence that had come in while I was away, but also dealing with the breakdown of the hub of my office. My computer died the morning of my return. Welcome back!

"Our experience out there was so intense!" I said to Ellen a few days later over a cup of steaming barley soup. We were sitting at a small wood and wrought iron cafe table in a local health food establishment, and Karl and I had just given her a blow-by-blow description of our trip.

"And now that we're back, instead of feeling empowered and invigorated and ready to tackle our jobs and lives with enthusiasm . . . ." Karl's voice trailed off.

Ellen blinked at us expectantly, waiting for one or the other of us to complete the thought Karl had left dangling in the air.

"We feel really out of place. Like we don't fit here anymore," I said, confused and feeling faintly guilty for being anything less than enlightened.

"But it sounds like the whole experience was more than anything you could have asked for!" replied Ellen, obviously not appreciating our discomfort.

"Yeah," I half-heartedly agreed. This was precisely why I felt guilty. Karl and I had just experienced an extraordinary trip, no question about it. And while we'd tried our best to go out to New Mexico with no expectations or pre-conceived ideas of what we wanted to have happen to us, we had, indeed, hoped to return to Pennsylvania transformed, preferably with a new and improved perspective on our lives and where we were going.

Instead we'd come back to the same stuff we'd left. Only now, maintaining the status quo was even more painful and uncomfortable. Nothing fit anymore. Even friendships and relationships with clients and business associates were changing.

Almost as if on cue, Beth, our mutual friend and fellow studymate, unexpectedly walked into the deli.

"Hi!" I said quickly, maybe a little too enthusiastically, as soon as we made eye contact. Inside, my heart sank and I felt like I'd been caught with my hand in the cookie jar. I could see from Beth's expression that she was upset that Karl, Ellen and I were meeting and talking without her.

"Hi Beth!" chimed in Ellen and Karl. "I tried to call you back the other day," Ellen continued, "but your line was busy."

Beth just looked at us, her usually wide, full-mouthed grin replaced with an expressionless slit and hard eyes.

"We just got together at the last minute," I said, somewhat sheepishly. "I didn't have a chance to give you a call." I tried to sound apologetic, but it was a lie. I knew it and she knew it.

My relationship with Beth was yet another area of discomfort and distress to me since returning from our trip. Again, something was different, but I couldn't put my finger on it.

I'd had a reasonably long conversation with Beth the day before, during which she had done most of the talking and I'd been mostly silent, heeding a warning from somewhere deep within to keep the details of our Taos experience to myself. The more I learned about energy and consolidating my personal power, the more I understood the wisdom of maintaining silence. While I had no logical reason to behave differently toward Beth, I had to admit to myself that I'd gotten a weird sense from her during our conversation, as if I couldn't—or shouldn't—trust her anymore. It was strange, but it was such a strong feeling that it demanded my attention. Although I didn't understand it, I decided I should trust my intuition and see where it led me.

Easier said than done.

"How can I just turn my back on her?" I'd asked Karl, after hanging up the telephone and describing my unexpected distrust of our friend.

"Well what did she say exactly, Lis?"

"It's not what she said. She pretty much talked about typical things that Beth talks about. You know, the kids, her work on Catherine's courses and stuff.

"No," I continued thoughtfully, "it wasn't what she talked about at all. It was more the way she said it."

I'd paused, thinking back on our conversation, trying to pinpoint exactly what had bothered me. "She sounded fake," I concluded. "Her words were her usual happy, chatty Beth-talk, but there was a deadness to her voice that made me feel creepy," I said with a shudder. "And she was pushy about wanting to know 'all the details' of our trip, which made me want to clam up completely."

"You didn't go and tell her much, did you?" Karl had asked, looking up from the mail he was opening while I talked. His voice had an edge to it, and I braced myself for a comment about how I tend to talk too much sometimes, dissipating the energy of an experience or idea.

"No, I stuck to the generalities and told her I'd tell her the details some other time." I'd wanted to add a biting, "Are you satisfied?" but stopped myself. I hadn't wanted to start a fight with Karl over this. Lately, though, the weight of his judgment had been getting too great to bear without comment. There were times when he seemed disdainful of me for failing to be completely silent about the details of my life, which frustrated me. His connection to our handful of friends was mostly through me, and a large part of maintaining relationships is through a mutual sharing of feelings, ideas, and experiences. It's an interesting balancing act to be a true friend yet maintain a certain level of silence as to the details of one's life.

So it was within this context that we all watched Beth walk out the deli door. "Man, was that ever unpleasant," I muttered out loud.

"Oh, she'll be OK," said Ellen, off-handedly dismissing the incident.

"I don't know," I insisted, shaking my head. "Her feelings were hurt. It was written all over her face."

"There's nothing we can do about it now," Karl said.

"How would you feel, though?" I asked, looking from Ellen to Karl and back to Ellen again. "I'd feel hurt and left out."

"Yes, I suppose I would," agreed Ellen, and then facetiously blurted, "But she shouldn't have come in here for lunch!"

We laughed at Ellen's comment, but her attitude both surprised and saddened me somehow.

Three or four days later, Ellen called to tell me that Catherine, our metaphysical teacher, was definitely coming to New Hope to give a lecture in three weeks. The plans being made between Catherine, Beth, and a few other of Catherine's students called for two one-day workshops, the first for the general public, the second just for us, her students. She was going to allow us to take an oral examination on whatever course we were working on at the moment.

"It seems that Beth and Catherine are getting quite chummy," Ellen remarked. There was a clipped tone to her comment that broadcast loud and clear her displeasure with the rapport developing between Beth and our teacher.

"Does that bother you?"

"Of course not!" Her response was quick.

"Are you sure?" I needled.

"Well, maybe a little bit," she confessed. "It's just that I've known Catherine much longer than Beth has, but in just the past several months Beth's become so friendly with her that she calls Catherine up on the telephone without even giving it a second thought!"

"If you want to talk to Catherine then why don't you just call her?"

"I can't! It seems too familiar or disrespectful or something." Ellen struggled to put a finger on her discomfort. "She is this extremely well-read metaphysician, known across the country for her brilliant abilities as an Etheric Translator, whom I respect immensely. She is my teacher. I admire her. I never called up any of my professors at college for an afternoon chat and I don't feel comfortable doing it to Catherine, either."

"I know what you mean," I agreed. "I don't have the comfort level with Catherine that Beth does, either."

"Well, you've apparently been a topic of discussion between the two of them, too," Ellen said.

This was a twist to the conversation that I hadn't expected.

"What do you mean?" I asked quickly, feeling anxious and hating how it reflected in my voice.

"Beth thinks you've been acting weird since you returned home from your trip."

"Oh?"

"She's said it to me, too, but I just told her I hadn't noticed." I couldn't tell from this comment whether Ellen agreed with Beth or not.

"How have I been acting weird?" Defensiveness kicked in, despite my efforts to remain detached. "Geez, just because I'm not as talkative as she'd like me to be . . . ." It irritated me that my behavior was being discussed and, perhaps worse, criticized.

"It's really been bothering Beth," Ellen persisted. "So apparently she talked to Catherine about it and Catherine told Beth to remember that you have the owl."

"What?!?" Suddenly, my heart started to race and I felt over-whelmed with outrage—and a chilling uneasiness.

"I know! Isn't that a strange thing for her to say?" continued Ellen. " '*Remember, she has the owl,*' that's what Beth said. I know 'cause I asked her to repeat it. And when I asked her what Catherine meant by that, Beth's voice changed and she said she had to go. She hung up right after that."

"You don't know how odd that truly is, Ellen," I said uneasily. "Catherine has never, ever spoken to me directly about the owl I found. When I asked her for input on what that particular bird signifies metaphysically, she only faxed me some generic, textbook-type information." I paused. "Remember that?" I prodded, knowing I'd related this to her when it happened. "Remember how I asked Catherine to tell me how she would interpret my discovery and she never got back to me on it? I'm amazed now that she even remembered the incident, much less gave it such significance that she'd bring it up to Beth."

"Well . . .?" said Ellen with a shrug in her voice.

"Well?!" I asked back, echoing her response. "What do you think she meant by it? The way you make it sound, it feels like she thinks it's bad that I found the owl. And what is so significant about the owl that she's mentioning it to Beth???"

"I'm sure I don't know, Lisa," Ellen answered, a mixture of boredom and irritation creeping into her voice.

I didn't know what to say. My mind was running a hundred miles an hour and I felt like I was in a Twilight Zone episode. Didn't Ellen recognize how weird this all sounded?

"I've gotta go," I heard Ellen's voice say into my ear. "Maybe we can get together some afternoon later this week and study," she suggested, sounding as if she had no idea of the devastation this conversation left in its wake.

"OK, give me a call," I played along. But when I hung up the phone a wave of nausea washed over me.

CHAPTER SIXTEEN

"**D**on't come then!" I shouted at Karl, the exasperation in my voice bouncing off the kitchen cupboards in jagged spikes.

Anger, frustration. Red, ugly irritation swirled around us.

Karl roared back at me, his eyes flashing, "Don't you hear me?"

"I think I do!" I screamed at him. "Stay home if that's what you want—Just quit blaming me for your being miserable!"

My eardrums rang in the silence that followed. The words of our fight kept reverberating through my mind. I couldn't decide which of the emotions they expressed should take precedence: anger, disappointment, sadness, loneliness . . . fear for our marriage.

It was 4:30 a.m., so the silence surrounding us was deep and dark. We were up because our 9 year old had thrown up several times half an hour earlier. After we'd comforted him, cleaned things up, and gotten him back to bed, we'd both been unable to get back to sleep. It was Friday, and our conversation had turned toward Catherine's upcoming lecture the next day, as well as the oral examinations, or 'seminary' work, as Catherine liked to call it, to be done on Sunday.

In the three weeks since we'd been home from New Mexico, our relationship had grown increasingly distant and testy. While there were moments when we were great together, really feeling on track and excited about our studies, most of the time it seemed to be getting harder for us to live our lives in harmony with our newfound beliefs. Our interaction tonight—or rather this morning—was becoming more the rule than the exception.

"It seems like every single weekend we're doing something. Running here, running there, visiting your parents, seeing your sister," Karl complained. "I'm sick of it all!" He spat the words out harshly as he pawed though the bills and junk mail piled on our kitchen table. Finding his pack of Kent IIIs hiding under the electric bill, he shook the pack, took one out and patted himself absentmindedly, apparently expecting to find a pack of matches in his teeshirt or underwear. "I just want to stay home and rest. I'm tired. I don't want to have to see or talk to one more person." He walked across the kitchen and lit his cigarette on one of the gas burners on our stove. And to think this all started because I had commented that I still needed to read another book on our assigned reading list if I expected to be tested by Catherine on Sunday. I never should have brought it up.

He wasn't finished. "And now we have to go to Catherine's thing." Karl emphasized our teacher's name with such a sneer in his voice that I was taken by surprise. "Catherine this. Catherine that. Maybe we should just forget all of this stuff that we're learning and go back to the real world." Two streams of blue smoke blew forcefully from his nostrils.

We were at a standoff. My retort that he just stay home and stop blaming me for his misery echoed hollowly in my ears. I felt lonely. Isolated.

His rage seemed so out of proportion to the situation. There was nothing more I could say. I wanted him to come with me this weekend but not if he felt this way.

"Maybe I'll just go to the thing on Sunday," he said suddenly, squashing his cigarette butt in the ashtray. A lone ember burned relentlessly and it seemed as though its single tendril of smoke deliberately kept going in my eyes. "One of us should stay home with the boys on Saturday if they're going to be sick like this."

"Sure. You do that." I walked across the kitchen and opened the door to the stairs up to our bedroom. We both knew he'd do what he wanted, regardless of what I preferred. I was too worn out to argue anymore. And how could I, anyway, when he used the kids as an excuse? "Love you," I said softly.

Truth be told, I was nervous enough about seeing Catherine this weekend without having to deal with Karl's resentment over being there.

"Love you too," he replied, staring out our kitchen door into the pre-dawn blackness.

It sounded as strained as it felt.

CHAPTER SEVENTEEN

"The program begins at 10:00 a.m., so we should figure on getting to the hotel around 9:00 a.m. to set everything up and get organized," Beth instructed me over the phone later that morning. She had made most of the arrangements for this weekend, with Catherine's guidance, and I was willingly doing my part as a worker bee.

"OK, I'll be there. Do you want me to bring anything?" I asked.

"I don't think so. Just yourself. We'll need to make sure the tables are set up in the back to display the books for sale and the jewelry Catherine's bringing with her. I'll also need someone to collect attendance fees and give out name tags." Beth's voice trailed off and she sounded somewhat distracted. "And we're selling raffle tickets."

"To what?" I knew one job I wasn't going to do. I hate selling things.

"One of the pieces of jewelry from Catherine's collection. We're going to give the proceeds to a homeless shelter."

"That's a nice idea," I said agreeably. Beth and I had pretty much moved on with things over the past couple weeks. We never specifically talked about the deli incident, and she never gave me any hint that she'd been talking to Catherine—and Ellen— about me. All our conversations since then had centered on the upcoming "Catherine Weekend," as we called it, our worries over getting all of our assignments completed, and ironing out last minute details for the public seminar.

I was torn between wanting to bring everything out in the open so we could deal with it, and wanting to simply be silent and watch it all unfold. Would Beth ever say anything to me directly? Would she ever come out and admit to me that she thought I was acting 'weird?' Would Catherine make any comment to me or treat me differently in any way? Would anybody simply be honest and above-board with me about their thoughts and feelings?

I had to try to snatch a few minutes with Catherine alone during this weekend. Surely my teacher would speak to me freely if given the opportunity?! Maybe she would give me more information on my owl, since I knew by her comment to Beth that she was making a conscious connection between me and the bird.

The last thing I wanted to do was add to the friction beginning to manifest among the 'group' of us who were Catherine's students. But the bond between Beth and Catherine was growing tighter by the day, and I could sense how difficult it was going to be for me to speak with my teacher alone.

But surely this was simply Beth's insecurities coming into play. Of course Catherine could see what was going on! She was just waiting to see me in person. Yes, that was it. She wasn't going to rush to any rash judgments about me based upon Beth's comments!

The warning to Beth to remember that I was the owl was probably misconstrued by either Beth or Ellen. It wasn't as ominous as it seemed. The more I thought about it, the more optimistic I tried to become about the weekend. *Catherine is our Teacher*, I thought to myself. *Teachers are wise and dedicated to growth and, well, enlightenment! This has all the makings of a great teaching—and healing—opportunity. I'm sure this will all work out exactly the way it's supposed to. Neat and clean and wonderful.*

CHAPTER EIGHTEEN

Fifteen minutes before the seminar was to begin, I realized for the first time that things really were starting to get a little strange and that I just might not get an opportunity to speak with Catherine as I'd hoped. The early morning had flown by in setting up the seminar room, creating a display for Catherine's jewelry and selected books from her mail-order bookstore, registering participants, and selling chances for the door prize.

Five out of the seven people who lived on the East Coast and were currently studying under Catherine were present and helping out both in setting up and running the program. Karl was at home with our kids and planned to arrive later in the day for the second half of the lectures, and Ellen, who'd assured us she'd be here to help, had not yet arrived.

Beth was most definitely in charge. It was as if she had the only direct link to our teacher and no one—not even one of Catherine's other students—was going to see, speak to, or make contact with Catherine without Beth's clearance. It was bizarre.

When I asked where Catherine was that morning I was told she was 'resting.'

"Resting?" I said, trying to hide the surprise in my voice. "When did she get into town?"

"Last night," replied Beth primly. "She came to my house because she knew the way from last time."

"Neat." I could tell Beth was relishing her newfound status as 'the Chosen One,' and I struggled to hide my irritation with her attitude.

"We had dinner together but she was totally worn out from the drive. I rubbed her feet for awhile . . . they were sore and swollen . . . and she started to fall asleep."

"Oh dear."

"Yes," Beth sighed, "so even though I begged her to stay overnight at my house, she insisted on getting a room here at the hotel. I suppose it's for the best," Beth's voice cracked and I was amazed to notice tears welling up in her eyes. "She'll be able to take small rests at the breaks during the day today, and since she has a room right here, she can lay down and maybe even nap if she needs to."

I excused myself on the pretext of taking care of some people coming in to register, but actually I couldn't stand to listen to one more word. Wow. This was getting weird. If I didn't know better, I would think Catherine was on her deathbed. At the most, she was probably in her early 60's. She was in excellent physical shape and not, to my knowlege at least, suffering from any life-threatening illnesses. Yet Beth was treating her like an invalid! The 'trip' that had supposedly taken such a devastating toll on our teacher's constitution was only a five hour drive from New England, for heaven's sake!

After registering the three women who had come in while I was talking to Beth, I once again focussed my attention on the greeting table. When we first set up this morning I'd made two separate receptacles for the money collected. One, a tupperware container, was where I thought we could keep the attendance fees. Beth and Brenda, both of whom had been in charge of receiving pre-registration requests and payments, had put the list of pre-paid attendees in this cannister. From this list Marie and I had made nametags which we set out on the table.

The other container for money collected at the greeting table was a plain, legal-sized envelope which I had marked 'raffle.'

This was where I had begun putting the cash paid for the door prize tickets. I'd been told, and was encouraging sales by passing along the information, that the proceeds were to benefit a local homeless shelter. As I returned to the table shortly before the start of the program, I was disturbed to see that the money was being collected with complete disregard for my, or any other, system. When I mentioned to Marie that the raffle sales were to be kept in the envelope, Beth, who'd walked up behind me, said it didn't matter since we knew how many raffle tickets were sold by the number of raffle tickets in the box.

"OK," I said reluctantly. "It just seems like it would be better if you kept everything separate right from the start. It keeps things from getting all confused later on."

"We won't be confused," Beth said sweetly with a broad, reassuring smile.

"You'd be surprised how easily things can get messed up," I continued, not feeling comfortable with the nonchalant manner in which the money was being handled.

"I said it's not a problem, Lisa," Beth said, her voice turning icy.

Clearly, this was Beth's show and my input wasn't welcome. I backed off.

Abruptly looking at her wristwatch, the money issue was dismissed without another word. "I better go and see if Catherine's ready to come down."

Once again, I did my best to shake off my discomfort. I glanced around the room, really seeing my surroundings for the first time since I'd arrived 90 minutes earlier. The meeting room itself was relatively spartan. Indoor/outdoor all purpose carpeting lay over a concrete floor. The entry to the room, at the right rear corner, was reached after walking along an equally barren hallway. Upon crossing the threshold, a registration table and two exhibit tables were lined up to the left in a single row, end to end, across the back. The left wall was made up of floor-to-ceiling windows. Since it was winter, though, heavy cotton drapes with an early 70's motif of loud loops of purple against a turquoise background had been drawn, presumably for the sake of insulation, and all natural light was effectively blocked, giving the room a flourescent overtone. We'd set up approximately 70 chairs, 35 on each side of a center aisle, five to a row. By my cursory estimate, I figured there were about 50 people already seated, with a couple still straggling in. *At least the seats are padded*, I thought to myself as I chose one in an empty row approximately a third of the way from the front.

Nearly all of our previous seminars with Catherine had taken place in private homes or in the basements of churches, and because a similar number of people had attended, those facilities had been somewhat snug. Nevertheless, those gatherings had felt festive and light, quite unlike the rigid impersonality that permeated this one.

Suddenly, I caught sight of Ellen, who had walked in only a moment or two earlier. She was still whispering greetings to a friend of hers two rows behind us as she slipped into one of the empty chairs beside me.

"Oh man, what a morning," Ellen groaned in my ear as she took her seat.

Here we go, I thought. *Now I get to hear how mean Stan was to her all morning.* Ellen never failed to give us painstaking details of the wrath her husband heaped upon her whenever she wanted to devote time to her studies.

"Did I miss anything?" she asked breathlessly, after recounting the herculean effort it had taken to smooth his ruffled feathers.

Before I could decide if I wanted to dress the truth in a sarcastic retort, Ellen continued anxiously. "Did you get to talk to Catherine yet? What's going on? Why do things seem so . . . ." she looked around the room with a puzzled expression.

I struggled to keep myself from providing Ellen with an adjective. I wanted to hear how she was perceiving this event, since she was approaching things with a fresher perspective.

" . . . pompous and . . . ." she grimaced, "*weird*?"

"You got me," I said, shrugging my shoulders, relieved that I was not the only person who thought things seemed a bit heavy.

A hubbub at the back of the room interrupted us. The rustling of Catherine's caftan was punctuated by the clinking and tinkling of the jewelry adorning her fingers, wrists and neck. I recognized these familiar sounds, as well as her characteristically throaty chuckle, while the procession was still in the hallway. Synchronistically, everyone in the room suddenly stopped their conversations mid-stream and looked up, expectantly.

It was, without a doubt, the entrance of a queen. Actually, High Priestess was the description that jumped into my head, but I blocked that out before I could think about it in any detail. While I was eager to see my teacher again, I felt a wave of discomfort wash over me as Catherine entered the room. She was accompanied by a veritable entourage of acolytes: Beth, Marie, Brenda, as well as some women I'd never seen before but who obviously knew—and revered—Catherine. They were all twittering about her as they approached the doorway, then hushed themselves into a respectful silence as Catherine made her way up the center aisle to the podium at the front of the room.

Ellen and I exchanged glances of astonishment as Beth adjusted the microphone self-consciously. Both of us watched silently as Beth gushed a heartfelt but, to me, entirely too adoring introduction to our teacher.

"Whoa!" whispered Ellen incredulously. Apparently she concurred in my assessment.

The lecture, which focussed primarily on basic concepts regarding reincarnation, human souls, animal souls, and Catherine's understanding of the evolution of consciousness on this planet, was essentially a rehash of other lectures I'd heard her give. I never tired of listening to these lectures because the information rang true and never failed to inspire me on to even deeper questions and study.

Yet this day I found myself phasing out of the lecture and remembering my introduction, some three years earlier, to the woman who would become my first, authentic, metaphysical 'teacher.'

CHAPTER NINETEEN

"**H**ere's her name and telephone number," Ellen had said, handing me a scrap of paper she'd torn out of the back of her wallet Daytimer. It was summertime and we were at the side of a local pool, watching our children cavort in the cool blue water.

"Thanks," I replied, looking at the name again. Reaching for my pen, I asked Ellen, "What did you say she is again?"

"An Etheric Translator; ET for short," Ellen grinned.

Guessing at the spelling, I wrote it down underneath Catherine's name, just in case the slip of paper got lost at the bottom of my purse. "And she does what again? Translates the imprint left on the ethers of every thought, word and deed ever made by anyone, ever?"

"Yup."

"That seems almost too vast to believe . . . ." I said, my voice trailing off as I tried to comprehend the quantity of data supposedly available to this woman.

"I know," agreed Ellen. "But the information is stored in what Catherine describes as a sort of cosmic library or vault; all completely organized. And she has a spirit guide who helps her gain access to whichever life or lifetimes will help you understand your present situation or question. It's an intriguing concept, if nothing else," she added pragmatically.

I held the slip of paper between my right index finger and thumb. I'd never had a 'translation' or reading done for me before, be it astrological or etheric, and I was both nervous and excited by the prospect.

"How many times have you had her do a translation for you?" I asked again.

"Over the past ten years I think I've had about three," she said, frowning a bit. "Hmm. Let me think." Ellen was quiet a moment. "Yeah, I'm pretty sure I've had three."

"And they were accurate?" I persisted.

"Well, how can that be verified empirically?" queried Ellen, assuming a most logical tone. "I can only speak to the fact that the information she gave me rang true deep within me. The past lives that she made reference to which were supposedly impacting upon me at the time of our sessions were so disparate, yet brought such an uncanny clarity to the questions I asked, that I know, for myself, that there is something 'to' what she does."

We were quiet as we watched the kids take turns jumping off the diving board at the far end of the pool.

"I figure she's either psychically gifted and actually able to translate these etheric imprints or whatever, or she's a fantastically talented storyteller!" Ellen added, chuckling. "Either way, it's worth the price to have the experience."

"You make it sound fascinating! I can't wait to schedule an appointment. Thanks for giving me her name and number."

"Sure," said Ellen, smiling. "I got Catherine's name from one of my closest friends . . . gee, it must be over ten years ago now. I've only passed the name on a few times since then. This isn't a subject I discuss with most of the people in my life," she added somewhat seriously.

"Me either!" I quickly agreed. "I can just imagine what the partners in my law firm would say if they thought I believed in this stuff!" I rolled my eyes dramatically, groaning to myself at the thought of having to deal with that revelation.

Although Ellen and I had been acquainted with each other

for almost a year, we'd only really started becoming friends over the past few months. Just recently we'd stumbled upon the fact that we shared an interest in the unseen forces of life—dreams, reincarnation, meditation, spirituality. Our discovery was a joyful one because it was refreshing and fun to talk to someone who actually shared a mutual passion and thirst for knowledge in these areas. We soon found it to be dangerous to begin a conversation at a time when we were on our way to other obligations because our excitement would invariably be sparked and we'd find it difficult to stop talking and resume our business.

Our conversations centered on subjects that most people didn't even think about, let alone speak of with someone else. But in each other we'd found a kindred spirit, a fellow seeker on the Path. Fortunately for me, my husband, too, enjoyed exploring these topics, and I could go home to him and continue the intriguing discussions that I'd begun earlier in the day with Ellen.

Another strength of our burgeoning friendship was the fact that we respected each other intellectually and professionally. I was a lawyer, she was an independent businesswoman. We both took pride in our ability to hold our own in professions where logic, credibility, and assertiveness were prized. We didn't perceive each other as the airy fairy 'New Agers' that are so often reviled or scorned in the media for their foolishness. We were simply a couple of people who had a glimmer of a belief that there is more to life than meets the eye. A greater purpose. A cosmic order to this whole experience we call life on earth. And we knew how energized it made us feel to explore these possibilities and open new doors of thought, theory and, most importantly, experience.

Thus, in the course of our discussions over the past couple of weeks, Ellen had eventually begun telling me a little about this woman, Catherine, who was capable of giving really awesome 'readings.' My interest was piqued. I was ready to make contact and, phone number in hand, I did.

* * *

Finally, the three week wait for my appointment was over and I was actually dialing Catherine's number. What was she going to say? Maybe she'd draw a blank on me? What if there was only gloom and doom to look forward to? Would she make something up then or would she tell me the truth?

Calm down, Lis, I'd said to myself as I listened to the first ring. *Take a deep breath!* The line clicked in my ear. "Hello, friend," answered Catherine on the second ring. Her voice was soothing and friendly.

"Hi," I answered back. "I guess you know, this is Lisa?" I asked, feeling somewhat silly. After all, I had made an appointment to call the woman at a specific time.

"Of course," she responded. "Did you read the material I sent you with your appointment confirmation?"

"Yes, I did." The literature described in basic terms the nature of etheric imprinting, how she translates the information, and her policies on the types of questions she discourages. I'd also read that I was to expect her to say a brief prayer of cleansing and respect, which was intended to create a sacred space within which she would perform the reading. Finally, the pamphlet included definitions of certain terms and concepts used often in the field of metaphysics. "There was some interesting stuff in there."

"Yes, well, I've found over the years that it helps for people to have a basic knowledge of the nature of this work and the meaning of various words and references that may come up during a reading. If there isn't even a rudimentary understanding of the concept of reincarnation and karma, then this whole process can be confusing and basically useless. Having said all that," Catherine continued, "do you have any questions either on the material I sent you or on the process itself, before we get started?"

"No," I replied. "I think I'm ready—if you are."

"Yes, I am," she chuckled.

An hour later I hung up the telephone and looked at Karl mutely.

"Well?!" Karl urged expectantly. He'd remained in the kitchen with me throughout the vast majority of my reading, but had become obviously frustrated by the restraints of only hearing my side of the conversation.

"I— It was— WOW," I stated simply, shrugging my shoulders helplessly. "You're going to have to give me a minute to get myself together. She said so much, and the information she gave was so uncannily on-point with my life right now, that I just think I need a minute to assimilate it all!" I got up from the table and walked over to the freezer. I opened it to get ice out and realized that I didn't have a glass in my hand. I shut the freezer, walked over to the cupboard and took out a turquoise plastic glass. Giving up the effort, I plopped back into my chair, sat back and started staring out the window, allowing my mind to slip into neutral.

Thoughtfully, Karl picked up on the cue of the empty glass in my hand and got me an iced tea, giving me some space. "She didn't tell you anything awful, did she?" he asked, concern in his voice.

"No, no, not at all," I reassured him. "Just give me a minute."

While I wanted to tell Karl all about the reading, I was having no success whatsoever in trying to force myself to talk. Glancing in my direction but restraining his curiosity, Karl made himself an iced tea too. He set both glasses down on our wooden trestle table, sat down diagonally across from me, and gave me a look that said he was ready to listen when I was ready to speak.

I looked at my notes. "Well," I began tentatively, "it looks like I'm in a situation that I've been in before, and the only reason I continue to be in it is because my soul is apparently a perfectionist!" I laughed out loud.

"A perfectionist, huh?" Karl chuckled.

"Seriously. I swear, Karl, without knowing anything about

me, she started right off by describing a life that I supposedly lived in the 1700's which almost identically matched the situation I'm experiencing now."

"What do you mean? In what ways are they identical?" Karl asked, his eyes glistening with interest.

I proceeded to describe the reading in as much detail as I could muster, using my hastily scribbled notes. Some parts were hazier than others to recall, as I hadn't focussed on taking detailed notes. My main goal had been to listen and experience. I'd known ahead of time that the reading would be taped by Catherine and that I could look forward to listening to it—and dissecting the information it contained—in a week or so.

The past lives and situations she had described were astonishingly useful in helping me see and understand the patterns of my recent experiences, particularly in relation to my career. And in describing the reading to Karl, I was seeing and understanding even more the connections between these realities.

"So then she asked me, 'What's it going to take, Lisa, for you to recognize that you don't have to stay in this particular drama anymore? You've played this part before, you played it well, and you don't need to repeat it again in *this* lifetime.'" I stopped, closed my eyes, and spread my arms in a long, delicious stretch.

"And that's how it ended?" Karl asked, wanting more.

"Yup, pretty much," I nodded.

* * *

Over the course of the next twenty four months or so our relationship with Catherine gradually grew from an essentially anonymous one to that of students and teacher. We began by listening to audio tapes of informal lectures she and various colleagues of hers had given in the early and mid-1970's. The lectures covered a broad range of basic metaphysical and spiritual topics, such as reincarnation, meditation, comparative religion, healing therapies, and provided an intriguing springboard for lively conversations between Karl, Ellen, Beth, and me. Catherine had also written a personal note when she sent me the tape of my first reading. In it, because I'd asked her if she could recommend some good basic texts in the field of metaphysics, she gave me a list of seven or eight books that she thought would whet my appetite and give me a good foundation for further studies. I read these books eagerly and passed them on to my friends.

Within that time I left my job with a law firm and set up my own practice, and gave birth to our second son. As busy as all of us were with our jobs and families, we still found the time to get together at least once a week, even if only by telephone, to talk about the exciting concepts we were learning. So much of what we were reading and discovering felt right. Each of us remarked at different times that it seemed as if we were *remembering* this material, rather than learning it for the first time. The more we learned, the hungrier we became for even more knowledge. These concepts made sense! Underlying everything we learned was a basic love for the spirit residing within all people, all creatures, everything in the world.

Occasionally Catherine would make reference to the years when she and her colleagues had run a metaphysical school in which ancient mystical teachings and esoteric knowledge were taught. Eventually, we learned from Catherine that she'd closed the school several years earlier, when it became too great of a burden for her to maintain on her own. The core of the faculty had dwindled over the years as a result of old age or death and the bulk of the responsibility for guiding the students' development had fallen to Catherine. Whenever Catherine spoke of the school or her departed colleagues a wistfulness would creep into her voice which made it obvious how cherished those times had been to her. But the two or three times any of us braved to suggest, or rather request, that she re-open the school formally were met with a reluctant but resolute 'no.'

Then one day Beth and I were having an impromptu lunch at Ellen's house. Our schedules had cleared unexpectedly and we jumped at the chance to spend an hour or so sitting on her deck, enjoying the scent of fall in the crisp October air. But as soon as I arrived, I sensed something unspoken passing between Ellen and Beth. They kept exchanging glances as we talked about the books we were reading, and seemed excited about something.

"What's going on with you guys?" I demanded, having just come back from the bathroom and noticed that they abruptly stopped their conversation when I came out the sliding glass door.

"Nothing!" they both protested too quickly. I just looked, silently, from one to the other. I knew something was up and I wasn't going to pretend I didn't feel it. Then again, there was no point in arguing. Either they were going to tell me or they weren't.

"Have you heard from Catherine lately?" Beth asked gently.

"No," I replied cautiously. "You're the one who talks to her the most." Ellen and I often joked about how easy it seemed for Beth to pick up the phone and call Catherine on the spur of the moment, while we were more inhibited about it, not wanting to presume that we could just call our teacher up to chat. "Why do you ask?" I narrowed my eyes and looked at Beth, then Ellen.

"Well," began Ellen, avoiding my eyes, "Beth and I both got a letter from Catherine a couple days ago telling us that she'd decided to reopen the seminary. We've been chosen to be part of the first class of ten students to formally study with her again."

"Oh wow! That's really cool!" I responded, truly enthusiastic. "Why were you afraid to tell me? When did you get your letters? What did they say, exactly?" I asked, wanting all the details. It never occurred to me that Karl and I were actually being excluded. Catherine knew that the four of us were good friends and were sharing the teaching tapes and soaking up as much information as fast as we could. Our letter was probably at home in our mailbox.

"We got them on Saturday," replied Beth, cutting herself off before she said more. I paused. Today was Thursday. A pretty long stretch of time since they'd received their letters. Why hadn't we been asked to be in the class? Why in the world would she ask Ellen and Beth and not us?

"You said there are ten students?" I asked, trying to make sense out of this unexpected hurt. "Do you know the other eight people?" I hoped that maybe we were part of that group but knew in my heart that Karl and I weren't included in the list of new students, otherwise my friends would have been more encouraging.

"No, I don't know the others," Ellen answered, sounding sad and condescending and puzzled all at the same time. "They're from all over the country—even Alaska," she added, as if that made a difference.

"Did you guys *ask* to be part of this class?"

"No," they replied simultaneously. "We were as surprised as you are when we got our letters and saw that you weren't included," added Ellen. "We thought it must be a mistake."

"And we didn't know how to tell you guys without hurting your feelings," Beth added softly, apologetically.

All of a sudden, I witnessed myself feeling angry and upset and irritated and hurt. But I didn't want to lash out at Beth and Ellen. I struggled to see this strange turn of events from a different perspective. *This is happening for a reason,* I told myself. *Surely Catherine knew this would cause a rift in our friendship— and hurt our feelings! She wouldn't do that on purpose, would she?*

"Well, hey," I shrugged, trying to shove these questions aside. "Tell me all about it! I'm excited for you. Can I see your letter?" I turned to Ellen.

"Sure," said Ellen, jumping up to get it. Both Ellen and Beth seemed relieved that I was putting it behind me.

While Ellen was in the house retrieving her letter, Beth apologized. "I am so sorry you weren't asked to join the class," she said. "I don't understand it at all. Maybe she thinks you're too busy?"

"Naaah. I don't know why she would assume that I'm any busier than you or Ellen," I said. "It's OK, Beth," I smiled brightly, trying to reassure her. "It's not your fault."

The sliding glass door whirred open and Ellen stepped onto the porch. She had an 8"x 10" manila envelope with her and at least seven or eight multi-colored sheets of typewritten material.

"Is there anything in the letter that says you guys can't show me your materials or talk to me about what you're learning?" I asked. "Are you sworn to secrecy by a blood oath?" I joked, trying to lighten the sense of separation between us.

"I don't think so," murmured Ellen as she glanced again at her letter of invitation. "Nope," she concluded and handed me the entire packet.

Catherine's letter was addressed to all ten of the students she'd selected (I realized then that Beth and Ellen had obviously known all along that Karl and I were not included) and basically stated that she was reluctantly opening the school again because of the persistent interest expressed by each of them. She went on to briefly describe what they could expect during their individualized correspondence instruction, how long she expected it to take each of them to complete the entire course of study, and what was required for them to begin. An application form was included, as well as lists of required courses, electives, and a history of the school itself.

After reading through all the paperwork, excitedly oohing and aaahing at the descriptions of the various courses they would be taking, I looked at my friends. "This is such a cool opportunity," I said earnestly, handing the packet of papers back to Ellen. "I'm really jealous," I admitted with a laugh, "but what do you expect? It'll really help a lot if you guys let me learn vicariously, even if it's just by reading the same books as you do."

* * *

I never did find out why we'd been excluded by Catherine. After about four months of listening to Ellen and Beth discuss their studies, I decided to practice a Universal Truth which was taught and advocated by Catherine: ASK—Ask and you shall receive; Seek and you shall find; Knock and the door shall be opened. I wrote to Catherine and *asked* if Karl and I could begin a formal course of study with her. Much as I didn't want to acknowledge it, I sensed Catherine's unspoken hesitation. For the life of me, I didn't understand what the problem could be. After waiting weeks for a response, we finally received a letter from Catherine. She made it clear that, upon meditation and a request for higher guidance herself, she was instructed to honor our request.

We were therefore accepted into the program and began studying in earnest the classic metaphysical treatises of Blavatsky, Akhilananda, the Essenes, and many others. Determined to learn as much as I could from this teacher, whose breadth and depth of esoteric knowledge impressed me so much, I deliberately refused to give any further thought to Catherine's initial, and obvious, reluctance to take us on as her students.

CHAPTER TWENTY

Startled out of my reverie by the applause of those around me, I glanced at Ellen, who was leaning toward me. "This was the same lecture that she gave back in November," she whispered, sounding disappointed.

"Yeah," I agreed. "I kind of got lost in my thoughts during the lecture."

"Well, I hope the rest of the presentations today aren't repeats because I could be using this time to review for tomorrow's oral exams. In fact, I'd rather be home preparing for tomorrow than listening to this stuff over again," Ellen continued, a testy edge creeping into her voice. I had to agree with her. My priority was also in getting ready for our exams. Up until now, all of our tests with Catherine had been in an essay format, with us submitting our written answers via fax or mail. Tomorrow was going to be our first opportunity to be tested orally, which would allow for verbal exchange with our teacher. None of us knew what to expect; but Ellen and I, being the competitive, grade-oriented high achievers that we'd always been, were particularly nervous and afraid that we wouldn't be prepared or 'good' enough.

I realized with surprise that an entire year had gone by since I'd boldly asked Catherine if we could study with her. Not once had I regretted asking, and I didn't think Karl did either, except for the times when, like the other day, he would lash out and say that he didn't want to be committed to doing anything with any-body. But that was probably stress. Although he wouldn't admit it, he was as nervous as I was over having to respond to Catherine's questions directly. When you're sitting face to face with your teacher it's a lot harder to dress up a bullshit answer and get away with it.

To add to the pressure we were feeling that afternoon, there had been recent correspondence from Catherine stating that she expected us to complete our course of study by the summer sol-stice. That was only four months away!

"Are you going to be able to finish all of your studies by the end of June?" I asked Ellen, as we took our seats at a round banquet table inside the hotel's dining room. The seminar had broken for lunch and, to our amazement, Beth and the two other women who had been fawning on Catherine earlier had insisted that she immediately retreat to her room to 'rest.' It soon became obvious to both of us that we were on our own.

Ellen was picking suspiciously at a scoop of chicken salad which had been plopped in the center of a bed of straggly-look-ing lettuce. "Gee, you know I was really amazed when I got that letter last week asking us to decide where we want to have our 'graduation' ceremony," she commented. I nodded my head in agreement and managed a grunt around my mouthful of club sandwich. Karl and I had also been surprised by the pronounce-ment that we should be wrapping up our studies. "I don't think there's any way I can get the remaining courses completed by then," Ellen continued. "It's not as if my plate isn't overflowing with other responsibilities," she added, defiantly jutting out her slender chin.

"I hear you," I said in agreement, nodding my head affirma-tively. "But really, with Metaphysics I and II completed," I continued, selecting one of the few intact ridged potato chips from the tangled mass of pieces and crumbs on my plate, "the rest of the electives look much less intensive. I was looking over them this morning because I was worried about finishing in four

months too, and I felt better after I looked at the remaining electives."

"I guess so," Ellen sounded unconvinced.

"There's no more *Blavatsky*," I said, pointedly emphasizing
the name of a pioneer in modern metaphysical study and one of
the founders of the Theosophical Society.

"Oh, thank God!" exclaimed Ellen, and we both laughed.
Wading through the *Abridgment of Blavatsky's Secret Doctrine*,
and then trying to answer essay questions on the tome while
sounding as though we'd at least somewhat understood it, had
been a major undertaking that none of us wanted to repeat.

"Seriously, though," I resumed my line of thought, "I'm certain we can get it all done if we put our minds to it. After all, we're
so lucky to be studying this stuff with Catherine as it is. If she
thinks we can finish by summer solstice then I tend to figure she
knows what she's talking about, since she's been teaching it for
so many years."

"I guess so," Ellen reluctantly agreed. I sensed that she'd
been working herself up to just bagging the whole thing. Quitting
was something she hinted at whenever she was facing the gun of
completing a course. "But I'll tell you what else is bothering me,"
she said in a quieter, confidential tone.

I cocked my head and looked at her questioningly. "What?"
I asked.

"All this talk about being 'ordained' . . . ."

"Oh yeaaaah!" I interrupted in a whisper. I'd momentarily
forgotten that part of Catherine's letter. "Isn't that weird?"

"I am really uncomfortable with anything that smacks of religion and dogma and hierarchy," Ellen said quietly, but
emphatically. She lowered her voice to nearly a whisper. "This is
part of the reason I love learning about metaphysical truths and
Universal Law and teachings that have been around for ages! It
rings true and it isn't tied to any one religion!"

"I feel the same way," I said, nodding in agreement. "When
we got into this there wasn't any talk about becoming a part of

the church." I was referring to the Trans-dimensional Church of Truth, which was the umbrella organization under which Catherine did all of her spiritual work and teaching. "It's not required, is it?"

"No, I don't think so," Ellen replied , her brow furrowing in thought. "But now it seems like it's almost sort of expected, you know? It's, well, I don't know . . . ."

"An honor?" I suggested.

"Yeah, an honor," Ellen agreed. "And I don't want to be disrespectful to Catherine or anything, but I really don't like the whole idea of being ordained a minister of anything, even if it is a church based upon universal spiritual teachings."

"I wonder what my son's catechism teacher would think?" I joked, a lingering uneasiness clinging to my words. Karl and I had immediately noticed the reference to 'ordination' in our last correspondence from Catherine and were rather unsettled by it. I was studying with Catherine because I deeply believe that all faiths lead to the same Universal Truths; that no one religion has a corner on the market of wisdom and truth. I'd always been uncomfortable with the concept that suggested that anyone who didn't believe in my religion—Roman Catholic—would either go to hell or be in limbo. Even as a small child I remember thinking to myself that the Church must be kidding, that there was no way anyone could really and truly think that way.

But my reference to the catechism teacher was not purely rhetorical. Karl and I made a point of going to church with our sons each and every Sunday because we believe that a strong religious foundation is important to both a marriage and a family. As a result of our studies, however, we were starting to question the fundamental tenets of the Church. We were learning about the remarkable core similarities of all of the world's religions. We were seeing that basic spiritual concepts we once believed be-longed only to Christianity had been espoused by other religions, even the dreaded 'pagans,' thousands of years before Jesus was even born. Most importantly, we were starting to realize the difference between a strong religious upbringing and a strong spiritual foundation in life.

Just two weeks earlier, while reciting a prayer during Mass that affirms one's basic beliefs in both the Church and its teachings, I found myself reluctant to say those particular words anymore, even though I'd been saying them, without really thinking about them, all my life. I realized with surprise that I no longer thought that the church of my youth was the one and only way to God. And even though I never seriously thought that Roman Catholics were better or more enlightened than anyone else, I was beginning to feel acutely hypocritical in continuing to state out loud a prayer I didn't believe in.

I'd recorded my discomfort in my journal and put the dilemma out of my mind. But a few days later my thoughts were once again focussed on the actual, literal meaning of the words of that prayer when my son asked me point-blank if they were 'true.' Preparing for his First Holy Communion, he is required to know and understand this particular invocation. There was an undeniable synchronicity between my own realization that I could no longer say these words in good conscience, and my son's learning and questioning the doctrines asserted by them. In short, I was having a crisis of faith. In feeling compelled to answer my son honestly I was being asked to identify what I truly believe. I was faced with the choice of embracing what has been the faith of my family for generations or standing firm in my newer spiritual understanding. Consequently, the idea of becoming an ordained minister in any faith was simply beyond the scope of my desired experience. I didn't want to deal with it. Just as I didn't feel like dealing with the repercussions if my son decided to share the details of our beliefs with his catechism teacher.

"No, Ellen, I understand your reluctance completely and feel the same way," I said out loud. I glanced at my watch and realized that our lunch break was almost over. We had only ten minutes before the next lecture, given by a colleague of Catherine's from Michigan, was set to begin. We paid our bill, left a tip, and retrieved our notebooks from under our chairs. "At this point," I continued as we walked down the hall toward the conference room, "Karl and I just figure we need to focus on completing the course work. If we get all that done and find ourselves at the point of graduating and becoming ordained, we'll decide then whether that is the appropriate path for us. There's no point worrying about it now. Anything can happen in four months."

That said, I would never have guessed the enormity of the truth—and consequences—behind those words.

CHAPTER TWENTY ONE

W e'd been at Beth's house since 11:00 a.m. and it was now almost 5:00 p.m. All afternoon Beth, Karl, Ellen, Marie, and I sat in a wide semi-circle in Beth's sunken living room listening to each other answer questions posed by our teacher, who constantly challenged us to apply the principles and concepts we'd learned in our assigned readings instead of simply regurgitating facts. It was fascinating to watch Catherine tailor every question to our differing personalities and experiences. There was no chance any of us would gain an advantage by allowing another to be questioned first because Catherine's queries were vastly different for each of us. Instead, we all benefited from the process by listening to each other's answers, the ensuing dialog between Catherine and the person on the 'hot seat,' and forming our own opinions and conclusions.

"Never, ever accept what anyone says to you about spiritual matters simply because they say so," Catherine reminded us again when Marie expressed concern over a line of thought that had given her trouble in a text, written by a revered Eastern philosopher. "I don't care who the teacher or author is—including me! *Always* check and verify what you hear against your own internal barometer. If it doesn't ring true to your higher self, then walk away from it," she said emphatically. "You always have the ability, no matter who you are with or what you are studying, to vote with your feet." This was a piece of advice which Catherine had stressed from the very first time I'd had a session with her. I'd heard her state it many times in her lectures and read it in the printed materials she'd sent out both prior to her Etheric Translation appointments and as part of the coursework. Rarely did Catherine miss an opportunity to remind us of our ultimate power to choose what is right for us personally.

"But I am uncomfortable disagreeing with the principles of such a renowned teacher," Marie continued, unpersuaded. "And the fact that the text was required reading for this subject makes me think that you must believe at least to some extent that his position has validity." She looked down at her hands, seemingly embarrassed at challenging Catherine on her choice of text.

"Ah, but that is where you are giving your power away, Marie," Catherine stated with a cat-like smile on her face. She shifted to the left in her upholstered wingback chair, gently dislodging a fold of her purple silk pantsuit caught between the cushion and the arm of her chair. "First of all, you are allowed to have your own opinions as to whose philosophies you believe or disbelieve, regardless of what I or anyone else in the world may think. Secondly," she continued, looking Marie squarely in the eyes, "you are making a huge leap in assuming that I, personally, believe or ascribe to everything I suggest you read."

"But—" Marie started to interrupt, but Catherine continued as though she hadn't heard her.

"In order to coalesce what we believe in our own hearts and minds it is often necessary to come up against something that challenges us. In defining a truly personal philosophy, our goal is to identify the world view that makes the most sense for us." Catherine lifted her gaze from Marie and shifted her focus around the room, making eye contact with each one of us. "Sometimes the easiest way to do that is to isolate those principles which you don't believe or which no longer serve your growth and highest purpose. When you come across a belief or principle which irritates you, it is often a clue from your higher self that the issue needs to be examined in greater detail." Catherine paused. "Do you understand, Marie?"

"Yes, I think I do!" Marie answered, a mixture of relief and awakening swirling in her voice.

"Good," Catherine stated, smiling warmly at her student. "Can you explain to me, then, the belief that you hold which is challenged by Swami Akhilananda's assertion?"

"You mean my own personal belief?" gulped Marie, put on the spot by Catherine's probing question.

"Precisely," murmured Catherine. "As I just said, you need to isolate the precise idea or belief within yourself that causes you to feel uncomfortable with the opinions or beliefs of others. It's not enough to say that you don't like what a person says, or that you don't believe what a person or church or nation espouses. You must dig deeper!" Catherine's voice rose only slightly, belying her passion about this issue. "Not until you know yourself well enough to recognize exactly what it is you believe—and why—are you able to make a choice about how you want to live the rest of your life. For as we choose to believe, so do we experience."

No one spoke. Beth's dog, Megan, jumped up from the kitchen and came into the room as if on cue, gently nudging her golden retriever snout under Catherine's left hand.

"What is it, girl?" Catherine chuckled quietly, gently scratching behind Megan's ears. "My charge to you then, Marie, is that you contemplate our discussion today and meditate upon your discomfort with Akhilananda's position. Identify what, in you, is being irritated."

"Alright," Marie murmured, sounding a bit disappointed.

Catherine continued. "For seminary purposes, you have passed this elective and may proceed to begin working on your next subject. However, before you formally submit any essays in your next course, I want you to prepare a brief essay on the underlying belief you uncover through contemplation on this matter. Once you have brought this belief into the light of your conscious awareness, I would like you to write one paragraph on your choice to continue holding this belief or entertain other . . . ." Catherine hesitated, choosing her words carefully, " . . . options," she concluded. "You may fax this to me. However, given our schedule I would encourage you to complete this task by Wednesday of this coming week."

Marie dutifully made note of her assignment, then leaned back into the huge pillows behind her on the couch, closing her eyes and exhaling a sigh we could all appreciate. "Now I can just sit back and enjoy!" grinned Marie, rubbing it in to the rest of us that her turn was complete.

Karl went next and gracefully fielded the questions Catherine posed regarding the Joseph Campbell video tapes on mythology, a unique part of our assignment. During Karl's examination Ellen breathlessly arrived, apologizing for interrupting and being late, and giving us a rundown of the difficulties she'd had in getting out of her house on a weekend. This led to her request, at the conclusion of Karl's round, that she be allowed to take her turn next because the only way she'd been able to convince her husband not to be angry with her was to promise to stay at Beth's for no longer than an hour and a half. Catherine consented, and as soon as Ellen successfully completed her examination, she left in as breathless a flurry as she had arrived.

Eventually the focus of Catherine's attention turned to me. As we spoke I searched her demeanor for any indication of why she would have made the owl comment to Beth just a few weeks earlier. It troubled me. I deeply wanted to believe that the comment had somehow been misconstrued in its travel from Beth to Ellen to me. How would I react, I asked myself, if I were the 'teacher' and two of my students were having trouble communicating? Wouldn't I listen to both sides before making a judgment, especially considering that both people involved were my students? I wracked my brain for a logical reason why this woman of wisdom and knowledge would blatantly foster a rift in my friendship with Beth. Why in the world would she act in diametric opposition to the harmony and enlightenment she preached?

I must be missing something, I told myself. My insecurities, against which I was constantly waging battle, had urged me to call Catherine immediately when I'd first heard that Beth was talking about me behind my back. But the soft, sure voice of centeredness and balance won out by suggesting that perhaps my teacher wanted only to wait and speak with me in person. It made sense that she didn't want to attempt a reconciliation between Beth and me over the telephone. She was waiting to see me herself.

But now the day was here and nothing was said. Not a word, not a flicker of reaction was expressed when I looked into Catherine's eyes, gave her a hug, and told her how good it was to see her again. Her greeting was warm in words but detached in feeling. Not mean, not angry, just . . . detached. I dropped hints, giving my teacher little opportunities to easily broach the subject without forcing her to disclose the confidence shared by Beth. I was sure she would seize one of these nuggets and use it to open up the issue. I was wrong.

Feeling confused, misunderstood, and unfairly judged, my mind searched for a way to clear the air without giving away that I knew I'd been the subject of conversation and speculation. I felt certain that if Catherine would only take the time to talk to me there would be no doubt about my state of mind or my intentions. The more my thoughts chewed on the details of this misunderstanding and lack of communication, the more determined I became to 'show' Catherine how much I had learned on my trip. Surely, I insisted to myself, anyone who knew me well— much less a gifted clairvoyant such as herself—could 'see' that any change I'd undergone had been for the best, had been *growth*.

Thus, as a result of these worries and concerns sharing space in my brain, I decided to conclude my interpretation of Joseph Campbell's "The Hero's Journey" by incorporating and describing my experience at the Taos Pueblo.

"So of course I nearly flipped out when this guy came up to me out of nowhere and told me to *know myself*," I said laughingly to Catherine, hoping she would see that I'd at least maintained my sense of humor. "There I was, having just completed a week of intense adventure and inner exploration . . . ." I paused, taking a sip of my iced seltzer water and quickly deciding how much of our week I wanted to divulge. In a split second, I chose not to give any details, to make no mention of the firewalk, or of recognizing, then sacrificing, my fear of failure or witnessing Jake's death. Instead, I concluded simply: "I felt I'd just been on a hero's quest. But the whole encounter with the Indian man left me much more shaken than I would have expected. Literally shak*ing*," I said, emphasizing the last syllable.

Marie and Beth murmured their appreciation of what I'd experienced, and my reaction to it, but Catherine was silent.

"Actually," I continued, unnerved by her unresponsiveness, "I don't know why his comment upset me the way it did." I looked at Catherine expectantly, hoping that my admission would encourage her to give me some insight.

She just sat there, looking at me, making me squirm in silence. Finally, after what seemed to be an eternity, she spoke. "Besides the obvious, what message do you think the man was delivering to you?"

I froze. Oh God, that was the problem! That's what I wanted Catherine to help me figure out! I didn't know why the stupid guy had said that to me and I certainly had no clue as to why I'd reacted so intensely. "I guess I took it as a confirmation of what I'd just experienced," I concluded, trying to sound more confident about my interpretation of the Indian's message than I actually felt. "That I'm on my hero's journey, which is the quest for self-knowledge."

Again the silence. This time, I could hear the tick, tick, tick of the mantel clock in Beth's foyer and the deep rumbling purr of her cat, which was perched on the back of the overstuffed chair I'd moved to for the questioning. "You failed," she said quietly.

"Excuse me?" I asked incredulously, a hint of laughter edging my voice because *she HAD to be kidding*.

Catherine shrugged her shoulders and looked upon me with what I perceived at that moment to be a smug, almost victorious expression. "The Indian and his message were a test — and you failed it."

CHAPTER TWENTY TWO

At first I was flabbergasted by Catherine's statement, then embarrassed. I wanted to maintain my composure and take it all in stride—or at the very least give the appearance of being unfazed by her pronouncement—and I wanted to cry like a chastised child. No one spoke, although I was vaguely aware of the discomfort permeating the room by my friends' nervous shifting in their seats and random shuffling of papers. As I sat in dumb disbelief at her assessment of my encounter with the Indian, Catherine gave me an assignment. She spoke as if unaware of the devastation her comment had wrought on my self confidence. I looked into her eyes and smiled, trying hard to mask my discomfort and disappointment.

"Choose nine animals from your totem necklace," Catherine commanded. My fingers automatically moved to caress the carved animals laying warm against my skin. I felt the necklace through the fabric of my fleece sweatshirt, reached in and drew the fetishes out into the open. "Meditate upon and write a story about each animal you select," Catherine continued. "Actually," she hesitated, as if searching for the precise words to clarify her directive, "I want you to allow each animal to speak through you, to you, telling you how they are here to help you and what you need to work on in order to grow in your understanding of this situation," she said impassively, her dark eyes meeting mine.

For the life of me I could not read any expression in those eyes. "You may be surprised at the light they shed on your hero's journey."

"Alright," I agreed, feeling an odd mixture of excitement and dread inside. Despite the fact that I was being given this task because I had 'failed' somewhere along the line, there was a part of me that tingled with excitement at the prospect of having to write stories about my animals. But would I be able to do this? Did I really believe that the animals would speak to me if I was quiet? Already, quick as a wink, doubt started to creep into my heart. I'd have to make stuff up, I thought to myself with an internal groan.

"I want to receive your stories within two weeks of today," Catherine concluded, reaching for her glass of lemonade. Shifting her attention to the rest of the people in the room, I was clearly dismissed. "Does anyone have any questions about what we've gone over?"

CHAPTER TWENTY THREE

The signs were small at first. Not necessarily subtle, but certainly dismissible, particularly when they pointed to something I didn't want to see. The images of my dream, for instance, though vivid, felt slippery as I reached for my journal:

> *"Ed, an old friend I've helped out in the past, is back in business. As he shows me his office, I notice that he has himself quite a nice little set-up, including a computer. I know, as he shows me around, that he wants something from me—my help, my ideas, my brain power—but I don't know what for sure. He is talking very nicely to me—shmoozing me, I think—but I feel wary since he's taken advantage of me before.*
>
> *For some reason or another he is scrolling through the contents of his hard disc and I see that he has indeed, again, taken something that is mine. I see before me, flashing in yellow, 'cd\TRUST,' which is the directory designation of an estate planning program I have in my computer at work. I realize he has taken my trust program, as well as other stuff which doesn't seem so important, but I don't say anything.*
>
> *The next thing I know, we are out of his office and into the office of his associate. To my utter amazement Ed*

actually starts asking me to either give him money or do his job for him! I am shocked and outraged at his audacity.

I am so incensed at his blatant attempt to use me again that I start to punch him in the face, yet I am filled with an awful, gut wrenching frustration because I am rooted to the floor. I simply cannot step back in order to gain enough momentum to pack a powerful enough punch to knock this person out of my life. I keep smacking him in the face, with no effect, when I am overcome with a bone-chilling dread that if I don't knock him out of my life for good he will come back at me in one fell swoop and either kill me or knock me out cold."

Awakening with a start, I looked at the red numbers of the digital clock radio blazing beside my bed. It was 3:19 a.m. Branded on my mind's eye was 'cd\TRUST,' and my body's reaction—pounding heart, clenched gut—bore witness to the fact that something precious indeed had been stolen from me.

The dream occurred two weeks after our 'Catherine Weekend.' Whenever I thought about that last encounter with our teacher, I felt uneasy. Something about the whole scenario didn't sit right with me. When I tried articulating my suspicions, though, to myself or to Karl, I'd be overwhelmed with self-doubt. Maybe I was just jealous of Beth or bitter toward my teacher because she'd told me I 'failed.'

"Have you talked to Beth lately?" Ellen asked me over the telephone a week or so later. In the light of day, I'd dismissed my dream. I'd thrown myself into my work as well and had tried to put that whole part of my life, my spiritual studies, my writing assignment, the weirdness I'd sensed all around me at the seminar, out of my mind. I didn't like what I'd felt, so I tried to ignore it. That had included avoiding Beth.

"Nope. I haven't had a chance," I fibbed, knowing Ellen wouldn't challenge me since she used that excuse all the time. "Have you?"

"Yeah . . . ." Ellen sounded unsure, hesitant to continue. "But it was weird," she said, "and I was hoping maybe you had talked to her and could tell me if you heard it too."

"Well what was it?" I prodded. "Was it her tone? Her attitude?" I guessed, trying to understand Ellen's concern.

"I don't know," Ellen's usually brazen confidence wavered and I thought she might just let the subject drop. "I guess it was her attitude." She was silent a moment, as if weighing the pros and cons of going into greater detail. "Do you remember the raffle?" she blurted out.

The raffle? What raffle? At first I didn't know what Ellen was talking about, and I didn't respond because I was searching my mind for a reference.

"You know," she urged, "the raffle of one of Catherine's pieces of jewelry at the lecture that weekend?"

"Oh yeah," I remembered. "What about it?"

"Well, maybe I'm just being picky, but I talked to Beth yesterday and I don't even know why or how it came up, but she told me that she still hadn't 'gotten around' to delivering the money we collected for the homeless shelter yet." Ellen's voice was a confused mixture of indignation, disbelief, and worry.

"Uh oh," I said softly, but Ellen continued.

"She actually said she hadn't '*gotten around*' to it! Do you believe that?"

"Hmm . . . ." I stalled for time. I did not want to get in the middle of this. I didn't want to even hear about it or be involved in it at all. "Did she have a good reason?" I said hopefully. "Like, maybe, it was taking her a while to get the bookkeeping straight or waiting for checks to clear or something?"

"Yeah, right," snorted Ellen contemptuously. "I wish. That's why I was hoping maybe you had talked to her."

"Why?" I asked, again wondering why I was being dragged into this thing.

"Because her attitude was so cavalier," Ellen said. "It gave me a chill. It was almost as if . . . ." Ellen hesitated, clearly upset at even thinking this about our friend, " . . . as if she might decide *not* to give it to the charity."

"This isn't good," I said, stating the obvious.

"Lisa, I'm telling you, it was such a strange conversation," Ellen continued. "Can you imagine? I wish I could remember her exact words, you know? I'm so bad at remembering conversations verbatim." I had to laugh to myself. That was true enough. "But I was blown away when she intimated that, since they weren't expecting it and didn't know we had collected it for them . . . ."

"Whoa!" I said. "This is a major problem. She can't be serious?"

"I know!" Ellen's voice was urgent. "That's why I'm so upset."

"Does Catherine know about this?"

"I don't know," Ellen replied. "I haven't had any contact with her since that weekend."

"Neither have I," I admitted. "Doesn't look like we're going to finish our coursework in time to get 'ordained,' does it?" I laughed uncomfortably. "That's one way to avoid having to make the decision!"

"Yeah, well, I don't like to be pushed into making a decision like that," she said indignantly.

"Me neither." I laughed. "We are stubborn, aren't we?"

"Yeah," Ellen agreed. Her mood lightened just a little bit.

"I think Catherine should know about this," I said seriously, getting back to the matter at hand. "It's her school and her church."

"I know," agreed Ellen. "But who's going to tell her?" she asked. "They're so close . . . ." We were both quiet, contemplating the ramifications of this ugly possibility. "You don't think . . .?"

"Naaaah," I responded, following her train of thought. "I can't imagine that Catherine could have any inkling that Beth might be playing fast and loose with the raffle money. It goes against the grain of absolutely every single thing that has ever come out of Catherine's mouth," I continued. "Besides, can you imagine the karmic consequences of a teacher going against Universal Law like that?" I shuddered.

"Yeah, I know," Ellen agreed. "That's what bothers me. I can't believe Beth can even be considering it. We're talking basic law here, *what goes around comes around*,' if nothing else!"

"Not to mention man-made law," I interjected seriously.

"So what should we do?" asked Ellen. "What do you think?"

"No matter which way you look at it, Ellen, I don't think we're in a great position. First of all, we have to ask ourselves if it is appropriate for us to be butting our noses into something that (a) has nothing to do with us, and (b) may not actually be happening? Then, if it is, we have to face the fact that either Catherine is so close to Beth that she doesn't see it, or doesn't want to see it, and will very likely resent it if we point it out, or else she knows about it and is allowing it to occur." That thought gave me a pain in the stomach. "And if that's the case—"

"Don't even think it," interrupted Ellen.

"OK . . . so where do we go from here?"

"Will you talk to Beth? See if she says anything to you?" Ellen asked, a wheedling tone edging into her voice.

"I don't know that I'm exactly the person Beth is going to open up to, given the major strain that's been on our friendship since we got back from New Mexico. Besides, I'm not just going to call her up and say, 'Hey, I haven't called you up to chat for a few months, but how the hell are you and what have you done with the raffle money?' You know?"

"Please, Lisa?"

"No, I really don't want to," I said.

"You don't have to ask her about the money," she continued. "Just see if she brings it up herself. But more importantly, see how she sounds to you."

"Ellen, I've been saying for a while now that she's been acting different. But you've been busy telling me that she's been saying that I sound strange . . . and talking about it to Catherine, too." I was starting to get annoyed. Ellen hadn't seemed to care very much when I was a topic of discussion between Beth and Catherine. She hadn't done anything to find out what they'd been saying about me, nor had she defended me. I struggled to put those defensive emotions aside. They were irrelevant, really, to the conversation at hand. But I was starting to feel manipulated.

"Please?" Ellen pressed.

I sighed, irritated by her refusal to understand and respect my feelings, but seeing that she probably never would. "Alright," I agreed. "I'm not going to go out of my way to call her, but if an opportunity comes up, I will."

"Great! Thanks!" Ellen sounded triumphant.

"But I'm not going to ask about the money. I didn't have anything to do with the raffle to begin with, didn't even know we were going to have one until that morning, and I think it would seem odd for me to bring it up," I warned.

"OK, fair enough," she agreed, and we left it at that.

Only a day later, Beth called me to ask if I had a copy of a book we had to read for one of our electives. Catherine had told her that Karl and I had purchased the last copy from her supply and that the book was out of print. Our conversation lasted ten minutes or so and was enormously superficial. At least it felt so to me. Beth bubbled on about 'the church' and arranging more seminars, and the courses she needed to complete to be eligible for ordination. I was uncomfortable with the amazingly religious overtones to her side of the conversation. The focus and objective of her studies seemed to be taking a completely new turn; a turn down a path I had no desire to walk. Suddenly, the 'ordination' process was the be-all and end-all of her metaphysical education, the material she was studying incidental. Nothing was said of the money collected at the lecture. I didn't ask and she didn't tell.

Later that same week, I was sitting in a waiting room and picked up a copy of Yoga Journal. I don't practice yoga and had never read the magazine before, but there was a cover story on healthy eating that caught my eye, and I flipped the pages looking for it. The magazine immediately opened to an article about spiritual teachers and how some end up 'turning' and abusing the power they have over their students. I read the piece and felt disturbed by its content. I asked if I could borrow the magazine for the weekend so I could show it to Karl.

The primary focus of the article itself was advising readers to use *discernment* in their travels upon the spiritual path and to never give up listening to their own inner wisdom, the voice of their heart. The author encouraged readers to keep their eyes and minds open to the possibility that all spiritual teachers are, ultimately, human and thus subject to the same temptations as all other humans: greed, power, sexual appetites. That doesn't mean that all teachers give in to those temptations. But the ultimate power that we all have is to keep our own counsel.

"Most of the examples in here seem to involve sex," Karl commented, looking up from the article and reaching for his coffee mug, "but I can see why you felt it might be something we should read." He sipped his coffee thoughtfully, his gaze focussing on the clumps of daffodils that had poked their not-yet-bloomed heads out of the ground only days before.

"I guess I was surprised to read how well respected and authentic some of these teachers were when they suddenly seemed to go out of control," I said. "I always assumed that teachers like that were obvious sleazeballs."

"Yeah, me too," Karl agreed. "But I guess it's something that can happen to . . . anybody." Our eyes met for a long moment.

"I hate thinking this way," I groaned, getting up to get a jacket. We were sitting on our porch and though I already had a sweatshirt on, suddenly I was deeply chilled. "Are you cold? Can I get you a sweatshirt or something?" I asked Karl.

"No, I'm OK. Thanks." He turned his attention back to the magazine in his lap.

I was in the house for a few minutes, tending to the cereal needs of the boys, who had awakened while we were out on the porch. As soon as the kitchen door swung closed behind me I could see that Karl had finished the article. "So what's your overall impression?"

"Discernment, discernment, discernment," he laughed softly, uncomfortably. "It's ironic that a lesson emphasized so much by Catherine would be the one we'd end up needing to apply to her," he said.

"But maybe we're just being paranoid," I suggested. "Maybe I'm overreacting to her coldness toward me at the last examination."

"Maybe," he said thoughtfully, glancing again at the title of the article, "but I doubt it. If you think about it, you've been bending over backwards to give her all sorts of chances to redeem herself."

"What do you mean?"

"The whole way she handled this thing with Beth after we got back from New Mexico," he said, "as a 'for instance.' What kind of teacher with any integrity talks about one student to another and then pretends that it never happened?"

I shrugged my shoulders.

"Lisa," Karl said with some exasperation, "you kept telling yourself that Catherine was waiting to talk to you about Beth's concerns when she had a chance to see you in person. But when you met face to face she *never brought it up.* Instead, she undermined your confidence in yourself. She told you point blank that your interpretation of something that happened in your life was wrong. That you'd failed in your assessment. And did she help you flesh it out, ask you questions that would guide you to the understanding she apparently thought was 'right?' No! She gave you an assignment four weeks ago that you've been procrastinating about and she's never again brought it up. Not once has she nudged you or even, for heaven's sake, *contacted* you again! Don't you think that's a bit odd for a teacher?"

I sat on the glider swing, stunned by the conviction in Karl's voice. Although we'd talked about all of these things I never really thought that he gave them much thought beyond our conversations.

"She didn't bring up your owl, either, even though she spoke of it to Beth and made it sound like it was something she should be wary of." Karl snorted. "Do I think it's possible that maybe our teacher has become seduced by power in some way? You bet I do." I looked at him in surprise. "Do I think you would stoop to discrediting her as a teacher simply because you weren't happy with an examination session?" he asked, looking me squarely in the eye. "NO."

"I'm not looking to discredit her," I began, wanting to explain the heaviness of my heart in even entertaining the possibility that Catherine was not holding to the highest ethical and spiritual standards. "I hate this. I have had only the highest respect for her and her wisdom and abilities for years now. I don't want to think ill of her—*I trust her!*"

"I know!" agreed Karl. "I know, Lis. But you're being given messages. You're being shown that you—all of us, for that matter—must use discernment, even when it means seeing what we don't want to see."

At that moment I had yet to make the conscious connection that, in my dream, my *trust* had been stolen.

CHAPTER TWENTY FOUR

Perhaps I resented Catherine's statement that I'd failed. Perhaps I was simply busy in my day-to-day life, taking care of the responsibilities that all lawyers, parents, wives, and daughters deal with on a regular basis. Perhaps I was steadfastly intent upon refusing to listen—to my heart, to my teacher, to the Universe. Whatever the reason, I found myself immersed in the myriad worries of the mundane world, completely unable—or unwilling—to execute the task given me by my teacher.

I wrote in my journal sporadically, allowing myself only five or ten minutes when I did, before falling into an exhausted yet restless sleep. Too many times to count I would awaken at 2:00 or 3:00 a.m., my head resting on the opened page of the notebook, my purple pen having slipped out of my fingers into the folds of the sheets of our double bed.

"And I haven't written my stories yet," I commented to Karl as we walked at a rapid clip along the dirt road near our house. I was trying to change the subject, as I had just described a particularly nasty confrontation I'd had that day with a divorce client who didn't want to pay me for going to court for her after I'd spent several days of preparation on her case. I could sense Karl's irritation. We were squeezing a walk into our busy schedules, knowing that it was important to 'us,' yet feeling as though our time would be better spent tending to the needs of 'everybody else'—our clients and customers and kids. Money was tight. Although technically our businesses were steadily improving, we didn't see it that way. To us, any improvements were too little, too late, and certainly never sufficient. It seemed as though the harder we tried to make enough money to be comfortable and to have time to spend on what we love and enjoy—our spiritual pursuits and metaphysical education—the further and further immersed we became in the ugly mire of worrying about how the bills would get paid and wondering if we were working hard enough.

"I'm not surprised," mumbled Karl, more to the forest than to me. Hostility had been rippling just under the surface of our marriage for weeks now, with resentment about our relentless pace grating on our nerves and building daily.

"What do you mean by that?" I retorted icily. *What the heck is the point of these walks if all he's going to do is make nasty comments,* I thought to myself. *I don't need this. I was just trying to make conversation.*

"Nothing," he said, refusing to elaborate, which only incensed me more.

"Come on, Karl," I pleaded. I wanted to scream at him, pick up a stone and bop him with it. I was so frustrated with the way our lives were unfolding. I hated the way I felt almost every morning, as though I were just rolling out of bed onto a mouse's exercise wheel, running my ass off and getting nowhere. I knew he was experiencing similar feelings; I could see it on his face every morning. "We've got to talk," I continued. "We've got to help each other figure out what's going on with us!"

"Talk schmalk," Karl replied with a scowl. "I'm sick of talking. That's all we ever do. Talk, talk, talk. Where has it gotten us?" he demanded, his voice echoing through the forest that now surrounded us.

"But we haven't been talking, Karl. We've been too busy to take walks, or it's been too cold or rainy out and we haven't made time to just sit and talk to each other," I replied, making a conscious effort to make my voice sound calm and reasonable. "And where has it gotten us? Not talking has gotten us here, to this point, where I just want to give up on everything and walk out on you because there's no point to being miserable day in and day out, doing work I detest, if there's no communication or relationship worth fighting for." My words hung in the air like the cracking of a dead branch.

"So what's your point?" Karl asked, still angry and not wanting to make the effort to communicate what was really bothering him. I stopped dead in my tracks when he made this comment, but he kept walking, staring straight ahead now, defiance emanating from his posture.

"What's my *point*?!" I screeched. His arrogant nonchalance infuriated me. "Don't you dare walk away from me!"

He stopped, turned toward me, and glared.

"The point is that there *is* no point! I mean, there isn't any point to what we're doing and how miserable we feel doing it *if we're not working toward some common goal*. I hate being a lawyer—and I thought it was because of my fear of failure. So I've consciously been trying to make and derive something positive out of my practice—but the bottom line remains: I hate it! Yet I wouldn't mind it half so much if you and I were communicating, if I knew that we were working together to create something that will allow us to do what we really want to do!

"But you walk around in the house as though you hate me, hate the boys, hate everything about our lives," I continued, allowing the words to gush from my heart. "What is it? What is going on? How could we have felt so empowered out in New Mexico and feel so totally shitty now?" I cried, the frustration coursing through my body making it impossible to hold back the tears any longer.

"I can't deal with this," Karl responded in a gravelly voice, turning on his heel and starting to walk down the road again.

I was floored. Was he really going to walk away from me like this? I felt like I'd been punched in the gut by his words, by his whole I-don't-give-a-shit attitude. I wanted to turn around and walk away, refuse to follow after him like some obedient puppy. I wanted to ignore him the way he was ignoring me. I wanted to give him a taste of his own medicine and make him realize that he was pushing me too far, hurting me too deeply, by refusing to honestly look at his feelings and talk to me about them. I was surprised and a bit repulsed at how quickly my deep and passionate love for Karl could turn into deep and passionate anger. I *hated* him at that moment.

But I wasn't going to give up. I had too much faith in our love and our potential, as a couple, to let him walk away from me without a fight. But I also knew that I couldn't pretend this wasn't happening. Something was festering between us and it needed to be looked at openly and honestly. The more Karl insisted that there was nothing to talk about, the more obvious it was that we needed to talk.

I stood in the middle of the dirt road for a moment, staring at him walking unhurriedly away from me. Without caring about the consequences, I sprinted, smacking him in the middle of the back with my fists, screaming at the top of my lungs, "Turn around and talk to me you bastard! I love you, don't you know that? I'm scared! What's wrong with us???"

He turned around immediately and grabbed me roughly by the shoulders. I was berserk. I was so angry and so frustrated and so sad to see our friendship crumbling that I didn't know what to do. Having secured his attention, I stood in front of him, sobbing. "I miss you so much," I said softly, my words muffled by the tears streaming down my face. "This isn't good; this is insanity. I just want my best friend back. That's the only reason I want to talk," I said. I crumbled into a cross-legged sitting position in the middle of the road, too exhausted to stand and fight any longer.

Karl dropped down beside me, never letting go of my shoulders, but moving his arms so that they were completely around me. We held each other in the middle of the road, silently rocking as I cried from deep down in my belly. Karl pulled away, brushed my matted hair off my wet face and out of my eyes and gently whispered, "I love you. I do! Oh, Lis, I love you too."

"Then talk to me," I said, squeezing one of his hands between both of my own.

"About what?" he asked, frustration rich in his voice.

"About what's going on in your head." I tried to explain. "There's been an edge to your voice for weeks now, and every time I ask you what's wrong, or *if* there's something wrong, you blow me off." I looked him straight in the eyes, a connection that he broke almost at once. "What is it?"

He didn't answer right away, so I stood up, brushing cinders from the back of my jeans. I extended my hand to Karl, who remained sitting in the middle of the road, but he didn't seem to notice my gesture. He didn't even seem to realize that I was standing. His thoughts were obviously spinning a thread that took him a million miles away.

I stood for what seemed like ten minutes, waiting for him to respond. "Karl?" I verbally prodded.

He looked up, his eyes flashing an expression of surprise. "I'm sorry," he said, shaking his head.

"Where were you?" I asked. "I hate it when I lose you like that."

"Just thinking," he stated matter-of-factly.

"Well, think out loud," I encouraged. "That's the only place we can start if we're going to figure out what's going on with us right now."

"But I don't want to fight."

"Why do you think we'll fight?" We were walking on opposite sides of the road now, the width of the road between us, giving us our distance. He didn't respond. "And who *cares* if we fight? Fighting doesn't have to mean hurting each other. If something's bothering you enough for you to be stewing over it, then it'll just fester if we don't air it out."

Winter was almost over, and March was making its debut

like a ram: not warm enough to be considered a lamb but not wild and wintry like a lion, either. Dark clouds blowing to the east scuttled above the tree tops and threatened rain. Our footsteps, scrunching along on the pebbles of the dirt road, reverberated through the trees and emphasized our isolation.

"I guess I'm incredibly frustrated," he stated finally, whacking at a stone with the tip of his hiking boot. "You just never seem to be happy anymore."

"What do you mean?"

"Think about it," he looked at me. "You're miserable. And I'm getting tired of hearing about it. I work hard all day too, you know? I don't love everything about my job either, but you don't hear me complaining all the time."

"Oh," I said, too stunned to comment further. We continued walking, silence enfolding us once again, at least externally. My mind raced with sharp retorts and tearful confessions of hopelessness. I knew what he meant, although I bristled at his comparison. I was miserable in my job, there was no denying it. Yet every day I *willed* myself to go to my office, do my job, be of service.

For all our practice in talking to each other, this was one issue that was becoming harder to address as time went on. I knew, now, why he'd been reluctant to say what was on his mind. Karl became annoyed whenever I voiced my deep unhappiness with my career and he always ended up telling me to just quit— but his attitude, whenever he spit those words out as a 'solution,' made it obvious he didn't really mean them. He'd joked throughout the first three years of our marriage, which I'd spent in law school, that he couldn't wait to have a rich lawyer for a wife. And even though that fantasy had never materialized, the mystique of being a lawyer persisted. Neither of us seriously considered my leaving the profession to be a viable option. There was too much time, energy, and hope invested in my degree.

"What am I supposed to say, Karl? Don't you think I want to love what I do and be passionate about my career?"

"I don't know anymore, Lis. It seems to me that you don't want to be happy about anything."

"But I do!" I protested.

"Oh, really?" he countered. "Then why aren't you working on the animal stories like Catherine told you to?"

"I don't know," I said pensively, "a couple of reasons, I guess."

"Yeah? Like what?"

"Like I have this weird feeling that if I don't contact her we'll never hear from her again," I said, relieved to have our attention deflected from my seemingly unsolvable unhappiness. "You know that something has drastically changed in our student/teacher relationship. Can't you feel it?"

"I guess so."

"Not to mention the messages we've been getting as far as discernment and teachers and all this weird business about ordination," I added. "And besides," I added quietly, trying to disguise my ugly little belief as a mere afterthought, "I'm not a writer."

CHAPTER TWENTY FIVE

The sharp *tack tack* of icy raindrops slamming against the tin porch roof called me callously from my sleep. Before opening my eyes I heard a gust of wind rip its way through the tall maples surrounding our house, hurling a torrent of drops against the roof and windowpanes. *Another crappy day*, I thought to myself as I scrunched my legs up tight to my chest. Finding a warm pocket in the sheets, I opened my eyes a slit and looked at the shadows dancing on the walls in front of me. Variations of gray. No sunlight. The trees, no longer stark and barren from the winter, had more and more leaves blossoming every day which, ironically, made today all the darker because they blotted out even the indirect light of the overcast sky.

I could hear Karl downstairs putting the dishes away, starting the coffee. The weird sound our coffee maker makes when it's finishing its task burbled up to me and brought with it the smell of Vanilla Nut roast. *Hmmmph*, I thought, *something special today. Why does he even bother?* I stepped out of bed and sharply drew in my breath at the chill dampness of the day. I wished the weather didn't so precisely match my mood.

Automatically, I began pulling the sheet up, then the blanket, tucking in the loose ends. Moving around the bed, I stepped over two pairs of sneakers, a pair of wingtips, one spiked heel and a lone soccer cleat, and began pulling Karl's side of the covers up, making them even with my side. The wrought iron latch on the kitchen door at the base of the spiral staircase that leads to our bedroom opened with a loud *clack* and Karl's voice called softly, "Do I hear the birthday girl stirring?"

"Yeah, I'm up," I said, the tone of my voice reminding me of Eeyore, the donkey in Winnie the Pooh. Oh man, I could barely stand myself.

"Happy birthday to you, happy birthday to you," Karl serenaded as he ascended the stairs, singing in a whisper so as not to wake the boys. He was carrying two mugs of coffee, mine with a little bit of milk, just the way I like it. "Happy birthday dear Lisa, happy birthday to you." He smiled at me with a big grin and handed me my coffee. "Special stuff!" he added, nodding toward the coffee, "try it and tell me if you like it."

I took a deep whiff of the brew. "It sure smells good." I looked up at him and patted the space beside me on the bed. "Come. Sit."

"So whatcha gonna do on your special day?" Karl asked, trying hard to be nice. *Not spend it with you,* I thought, but bit the words back. We'd had another wicked fight last night and gone to bed without speaking, which was something we vowed years ago never to do. But he was trying. I should make the effort as well.

"I don't know," I said glumly. "Work, I guess." I leaned over the end of the bed and picked up the two pairs of sneakers and the lone soccer cleat, letting them dangle off my fingers. "We don't seriously wonder why there's no space on our floor to walk, do we?" I asked, getting up to take the footwear into our son's room. I didn't want to get into a discussion of what I was going to do today. Our whole fight, again, had centered on how he was feeling stressed out and like he was 'working all the time,' and his resentment that I was so unhappy with my job. I'd even caught him smoking again yesterday, and he'd defended himself by attacking me and saying that, in essence, it was my fault he wasn't able to quit. After all, he reasoned, he is upset because I am upset, and surely he can't quit when he's under so much pressure.

I was tired of trying to defend my feelings. He wouldn't admit it, but I sensed that his irritation stemmed from the fact that I wasn't making the money that either of us had hoped I'd be making by this time in our marriage and my career. We had both assumed I'd keep us comfortable, particularly if I 'worked hard' and 'played by the rules.' But it wasn't working out the way we'd envisioned. We *both* had to work, all the time, it felt, just to get by.

It was getting harder and harder for me to hide my overwhelming unhappiness. I kept trying to figure out what was wrong with me. Everywhere I looked, it seemed, books that said, "Do What You Want and The Money Will Follow," or phrases such as "Follow Your Bliss" were in my face. Whenever I read one of those titles or heard one of those phrases, a little nugget in the center of my heart would shrink up, nice and tight, sometimes to the point of making me choke back tears. Surely I'm doing what I want to be doing, I'd tell myself. Who wouldn't want the opportunities I have, the education, the ability to be self-employed. Why aren't I happy and satisfied being a 'professional?'

My journal was rife with pleas for guidance. I kept asking for signs as to what I should do, where I should direct my energy and focus. Yesterday, one of the partners from my old law firm had called out of the blue and offered me a position. While I was flattered that the firm wanted me back and gratified by the offer, every fibre of my being wanted to run the other way. I was honestly shocked at my reaction. In fact, it was so intense that, paradoxically, I began to doubt it. Maybe I was wrong, maybe this was the answer to my prayers. Then last night, when I told Karl about the opportunity and tried to describe the magnitude of my despair over the prospect and my conflict about what I should do next, he voiced, with exasperation and then disdain, all of the logical, reasonable considerations I knew I 'should' make, and which my own mind kept repeating over and over and over again. The only concrete reason I could give for not accept-ing the offer was that I didn't want to give up the freedom of owning my own business. But it was more than that, and only deep down inside myself was I even vaguely aware of the truth.

As 'open' as I wanted to think I was to whatever the Uni-verse—or God—might have in store for me, the fact remained that I *believed* only two options were available to me: stay self-employed and work harder, or go back to work for another law firm and work harder. Leaving the law entirely because it was not giving me satisfaction on any level of my being, physical (mon-etary), emotional, or spiritual, was not an option. I refused to allow myself to see that this could possibly be the message. So I twisted the message to fit my belief about how things had to be. I tried to tell myself that the call out of the blue meant that I was to give up my own law practice and return to work for someone else, never mind that the offer caused a 'fight or flight' panic and a surge of nausea.

Last night, after getting nowhere, I'd given up trying to un-derstand. Nothing felt right anymore. I could not see how any of this could possibly be construed as guidance or a message. As far as I could see, it was all complete and unadulterated bullshit.

Returning to our bedroom, I found Karl sitting on the edge of the bed, sipping his coffee. "You're really going to go to work today?" he asked, his voice and eyes reflecting his disappoint-ment. "Give yourself a day off, Lis. Geez . . . ."

"No."

"It's your birthday AND Good Friday, for heaven's sake," Karl continued, frustration starting to color his voice. "Hardly anybody will be working today anyway, you know."

"I know."

"I was going to make a few calls this morning, but I thought we could do something together this afternoon—maybe have a nice lunch somewhere or something."

"Naaah, that's OK," I demurred, making sure our eyes didn't meet. "Sharon has off, so I'll have the office all to myself." I looked up from lacing my boot. Karl was staring at his mug of coffee, sloshing the contents around in a mini-whirlpool. He looked hurt. "This will give me a chance to catch up on some of the paperwork that's been piling up," I said, quickly looking at my boot and avoiding Karl's gaze once more. If we made eye contact I knew I'd burst into tears. *This way is better*, I told myself.

An hour later I was sitting at my desk, staring at the screen of my Macintosh, preparing a Contempt Petition in a custody case I was handling. As I paused to consider the appropriate wording of the next allegation, I raised my eyes from the screen and looked out the deep, colonial window before me. The day was getting darker and darker, and as I watched, rain started pouring from the sky in windswept sheets.

Jarring me from my reverie, the telephone rang a muffled cry for attention from under the several subfiles I'd spread all over my desk in search of dates and facts for my petition. Since it was a holiday, I debated whether or not to answer it. I didn't want to speak to anyone or fake a cheeriness I didn't feel. The only people in the world that I might be willing to fake a smile for today would be my parents who, I suddenly realized, might very well be calling since I hadn't received their customary birthday greeting before leaving for the office. I shoved the files off the phone and picked up the receiver. "Law office of Lisa Weikel," I stated with an attempt at a lilt to my voice.

"Hello there," said a voice I hadn't heard in over a month. Instantly, I wanted to kick myself for having answered the call.

"Hi Beth!" I responded immediately, straining to sound upbeat, or at the very least neutral. "Gee, I haven't heard from you in a long time. What have you been up to?"

"I've just been really busy," Beth said smoothly. "You know, with the kids and doing more and more work with Catherine and the Church . . . ."

My stomach tightened. *Here we go again with all that 'church' nonsense,* I thought to myself. *What ever happened to talking about our 'studies,' and referring to Catherine as our 'teacher?'* To Beth I said, noncomittally, "Have you been getting stuff done? Are you going to have enough courses completed to be able to graduate in June?"

"Well it's just making me crazy," laughed Beth, sounding very uncrazy and totally in control—very different than she used to sound—" but Catherine assures me that I'll be getting lots of extra credit for organizing and handling the seminar last month."

I'll bet, I thought to myself, remembering my conversation with Ellen. I didn't want to touch that subject with a ten foot pole. I just wanted to sound supportive and get off the phone. "You did a great job. And thank you, again, for having us over to your house the day after."

"Oh that was fun, wasn't it?"

"It was interesting," I managed to muster, hoping she wouldn't catch that I was waxing less than enthusiastically. "So . . . ."

"So it's your birthday today, isn't it?" Beth interrupted, catching me off guard.

"Yes, it is. Thanks for remembering."

"Oh, I have you marked on the calendar," she said breezily. "Planning anything special?"

"No, not really. Karl probably got me a cake. Maybe we'll go up to my parents' over the weekend." I hoped she wasn't going to suggest we get together.

"How are you guys doing with your studies?" Beth asked, unexpectedly changing the direction of the conversation again. "You are planning on being ordained, aren't you?"

"Well . . . ." I hedged.

"What's the matter?"

"I don't know," I said reluctantly. "I'm starting to become, um, *uncomfortable* with the whole idea of ordination."

"Why? What do you mean?" I could hear Beth struggling to keep indignation from climbing into her voice.

"Well, Karl and I have been talking about it and we're not

sure that we want to get into all of that," I answered evasively. I knew that every word I said would immediately be transmitted back to Catherine and probably distorted in the process. Instinctively, I felt the need to be careful of what I said and how I said it. I listened for Beth's response and was met with emptiness. There was a void on the other end of the phone—momentary, yet noticeable.

Then she switched gears completely, ignoring what I'd just said and cheerfully remarking, "It's been ages since we had lunch together. Come on, I don't want to sit and talk about things on the telephone. Let's pick a date right now to get together next week."

I didn't know if it was me and my foul mood or Beth acting strangely, but the distinctly tinny and false tone to her voice made me shiver involuntarily. I didn't want a confrontation, I didn't want to discuss Catherine or the direction of my studies with someone I felt I couldn't trust anymore, and I didn't want to make any commitments that I would later regret. "Gee, I don't know," I said glumly, paging through my date book. "There are some matters that are up in the air right now, and I'm not sure how my schedule is going to be working out for next week."

"That's OK, pencil me in on any day and we'll confirm that morning," Beth prodded, undeterred by my reluctance.

"I'd rather wait," I said, sticking to my guns. "I'll call you on Monday; how 'bout that?" And before she could respond, I added, "The holiday will be over then and I'll be more in the mood to think ahead."

"Alright," she agreed, and I could just imagine her bottom lip jutting into a pout. But unexpectedly, her voice turned steely cold. "I'll wait to hear from you. And—happy birthday."

"Thanks," I said again, uncomfortably. The click made it clear that our conversation was over.

"That was weird," I said to myself out loud as I turned my attention back to my computer. Grabbing my mouse, I closed the file I'd been working on and pulled up some old correspondence I'd written to an attorney in another case. I gathered up all the manila folders spread out on my desk top, noting the subfile headings, 'correspondence,' 'pleadings,' 'interview notes,' as I systematically placed them into the larger accordion file which was their home. Despite the odd feeling Beth's call left in the back of my mind, I found myself enjoying a sense of satisfaction as I placed the custody file snugly in its place, alphabetically, in the pull-out drawer of my massive filing cabinet. Keeping my files compulsively neat and organized was a sweet and simple way for me to feel okay about myself. It was the first good feeling I'd had all morning.

A sharp rap at the thick oak door in my foyer made me yelp with surprise. All my reclusive feelings flooded back into my body and I debated whether or not I should just ignore the knock. I wasn't expecting any clients. Most people don't pick their lawyers by dropping in on them off the street, and those that do—well, I didn't want to get involved with that whole can of worms. Had I locked the door like I usually do when I'm alone in my office, I wondered? The doorknob turned and I felt sick. But the door didn't open; instead, the deadbolt thumped comfortingly in its place, barring uninvited entry.

Get a grip, I thought to myself. I decided to open the door, reluctantly reasoning that it was obvious to whoever was out there that someone was in the office. The day was so dark that the lights in my office were beacons of habitation. "Hang on a second!" I called out as brightly as I could. "I'm here!"

A gnarly, bent-over man who looked not a day younger than seventy stood on the concrete porch. The pile of firewood stacked to his right, towered above him. Glancing at the firewood, then at the brass nameplate bolted to the center of the door, he barked out doubtfully, "This the law office of Lisa Weikel?"

"Yes it is," I confirmed, only because he bore a stunning bouquet of cut flowers—yellow and cream jonquils, bright orange and pink tulips, and sunny daffodils. They were remarkable in their contrast to the wet, gray day. "Thank you so much!" I squealed as I scooped the bouquet eagerly into my arms, reacting as though *his* name would appear on the accompanying card.

"Hang on a second," I said over my shoulder as I walked back to my office to retrieve a tip. I placed the flowers gently on the wicker sofa in the reception room and grabbed a dollar from my wallet. "Here you go!" I called out. But when I got back to the door, which I'd left ajar, he was gone.

I'd been so taken aback by his intriguing presence that I hadn't noticed how he'd arrived at my office, what kind of a vehicle he'd been driving. In fact, as I leaned outside and looked around, I could see no cars pulling out of the huge gravel driveway. Hugging my arms close to my body to ward off the chill, I closed the door against the drizzle, leaning my left shoulder against it and turning the deadbolt.

As I unwrapped the blooms from the clear, crinkly cellophane, I pulled the small card out of its envelope. I assumed they were from Karl. They weren't. The words "Have a special day! Love, Beth" were hand-printed on the generic card. *Now why did she go and do that,* I wondered to myself, as I retrieved a glass vase from the bathroom cupboard. *We haven't spoken in weeks, things have been strained between us since January, and now I've talked to her and received flowers from her all in the same day.* Something didn't feel right, but I chided myself for not simply appreciating Beth's gesture of friendship. Why was I trying to read something sinister into this?

I arranged the bouquet in the vase and placed it on the corner of my desk. Flopping into one of the two upholstered chairs meant for clients, I contemplated this unexpected 'gift.' Within moments, it seemed, the flowers lost their initial lustre and didn't look nearly so bright and cheery. I glared at them suspiciously, feeling gloom settle heavily all around me.

Sitting up, I reached under the desk and pulled out my leather purse. As I left the house this morning, I'd picked up our small velvet rune pouch and stuffed it into my handbag. Karl and I occasionally played with the runes, oblong bits of fired clay with ancient Nordic symbols imprinted on them, using them as a tool to access our intuition. Usually, we would each choose a rune 'for the day' as we took our early morning walks. I tried to keep track of the runes we chose in a little pocket journal. Sometimes the runes we chose made perfect sense right away. Other times, they took a bit of reflection to understand.

I decided to pick a rune on my day. Considering how I felt, I thought wryly, it wouldn't surprise me if I chose 'Isa' (Standstill) or 'Nauthiz' (Constraint), two of the runes which irritated me the most. Closing my eyes, I sat with the rune bag in my left hand and deliberately cleared my mind of thoughts, emotions, and images of people that seemed to crowd into my consciousness. I gently tumbled the runes about, inside their bag, with the fingers and palm of my left hand. When I felt they were mixed up enough, I opened the drawstring of the pouch and reached in with my right hand. Instantly, a rune seemed to pop into my fingers' grasp.

'Hagalaz.' My shoulders slumped. *Oh boy*, I thought, as I reached for *The Book of Runes*, by Ralph Blum, which contained the basic interpretations of the twenty-five different symbols. I knew from working with the runes periodically that 'Hagalaz' stands for 'Disruption' and generally not the gradual type, either. Turning to page 121, I read:

> *HAGALAZ. Change, freedom, invention and liberation are all attributes of this Rune . . . . The Rune of elemental disruption, of events that seem to be totally beyond your control, Hagalaz has only an upright position, and yet it always operates through reversal. When you draw this Rune, expect disruption, for it is the Great Awakener . . . .[T]he onset of power may be such as to rip away the fabric of what you previously knew as your reality, your security, your understanding of yourself, your work, your relationships or beliefs . . . .The more severe the disruption in your life, the more significant and timely the requirements for your growth. Another of the Cycle Runes, the term 'radical discontinuity' best describes the action of Hagalaz at its most forceful. The universe and your own soul are demanding that you do, indeed, grow.*

These stupid runes are so damn joyful, I thought sarcasticly. Talk about doom and gloom, hellfire and brimstone! The entire fabric of my reality is about to be ripped away? Ugh! A shudder coursed through my body and I stood up abruptly, flinging my arms out in a snapping motion as if flicking drops of water from my fingertips.

Part of me felt a hopeful satisfaction that something might be about to transform. Only yesterday I'd written in my journal that I felt on the brink of making major changes in my life—jettisoning my law practice, going back to work for someone else and even, quite possibly, leaving Karl. I was feeling miserable, and I wanted *everything* to change.

But there was another part of me, a much larger part of me, that felt frightened at the prospect of cataclysmic disruption. Mother of God, I thought, I don't want anything to happen to Karl or the boys. That would shatter my life. That would be the worst possible way for the Universe to show me that I should be happy and satisfied with my life; that I'm a whiner and a slacker and an unappreciative bitch. I love them so much! Has my selfish misery put them in jeopardy?

Paranoid thoughts swirled in my mind. No matter which way I looked at anything today, I couldn't win. I considered with disgust the two sealed letters I'd prepared earlier. *Mechanical drivel. Meaningless posturing.* My mind was a tyrant that wouldn't shut up. I felt guilty for questioning Beth's motives, for wanting to be by myself on my birthday, for wanting a change. I felt guilty for feeling guilty.

Stepping into the reception room I glanced at the clock on the fireplace mantel. *Today would be a great day for a fire,* I thought fleetingly, but discarded the idea. No, Karl might show up for lunch. Or Ellen might drop by. Vehemently wanting to be alone, to disappear, I decided to close up shop, mail my letters, and get my oil changed. Anything to avoid having to deal with people who knew me. I felt spiky, scattered, and seriously on edge.

CHAPTER TWENTY SIX

The second I tugged open the door of Sagittarius Books and entered the tiny vestibule I could smell the warm spiciness of sandalwood. Unheated and large enough to barely fit two people, the entranceway separated the bookstore from the alley on which it fronted. Local business cards covered its walls, offering services that ran the gamut from homeopathic physicians, midwives, and massage therapists, to psychics, astrologers, and tarot card readers. Flyers tacked to my left advertised ongoing yoga classes, a weekly discussion group for A Course In Miracles, an upcoming meditation workshop, and a Solstice Celebration that took place the week before.

Pushing open the whitewashed double doors into the bookstore proper, I felt the resistance raised by the nap of the carpet mimic my own. Why was I here? I didn't need another book to read—I had all the assignments yet to finish in my coursework (not to mention those stories you haven't written, mocked my ego) as well as a Carlos Castaneda book I'd bought here only a couple of weeks ago, which I was nursing each night in the minutes before I fell asleep.

Breathing deeply, I felt the incense wrap a protective arm around my shoulder. "Hi Stan," I said quietly, smiling at the owner, a friend cultivated over the years by my frequent trips to the shop. He was sitting behind the counter on a gray metal barstool, a text on macrobiotic foods propped open on the cloth covered wooden counter in front of him. The haunting lyrics of Enya filled the small store with a melancholy that precisely matched my own. Suddenly my sharp edges, my jagged feelings of anger and fear, welled up into my eyes, a profound sense of sadness nearly overwhelming me. I felt alone and lonely and all the more confused because I sensed that I was somehow imposing this pain upon myself.

"Hi Lisa," Stan said, looking up from his book. "How are you today?"

"OK," I mumbled, still not wanting to connect with the outside world. I deliberately allowed the briefest moment of eye contact, fearing both tears and talk, but not wanting to be rude. "It smells good in here," I said, taking another deep draught of the warm, scented air and allowing my gaze to sweep from Stan to the bookshelves. Immediately, my eyes were drawn to a book directly in front of me, the word WOLF, a part of its title, written in red across its front. This bookstore was small enough and my trips here often enough that I usually notice new additions and recent publications. Unlike most of the books on the shelves, this one was turned so that the front cover faced outward, compelling my attention.

"It's sandalwood," murmured Stan.

I barely heard his comment as I drew the book from its place on the shelf. It was the only copy, which I thought odd, since I knew I'd never seen it before. Usually a new book was set out with at least two or three of its siblings. Holding the paperback in my hands, the yellow eyes of a wolf stared up from the cover toward something beyond my left shoulder. "Shouting at the Wolf," I read to myself, "A Guide to Identifying and Warding Off EVIL in Everyday Life."

Oh, yuck! I said to myself, hastily stuffing the book back into its wide slot on the shelf. *Why in the heck did I pick that up?* I wiped my hands on my pants. *I don't want to think about evil!*

Seriously agitated, my insides shaking, and feeling as though

I could burst into tears at any moment, I turned my attention to the stacks of audio tapes on my left. Windham Hill, Enya, Kitaro. The names floated before my eyes as my mind whirled in a frenzy. I repeated the titles to myself, but nothing was registering. My eyes landed on a tape with Wolf in its title. I looked away, willing myself to forget the book and to leave this place.

"Want to hear something different?" asked Stan, misreading my perusal of the tapes and interrupting my internal debate.

"Ummm. Gee, I don't care."

"With this dark day, Enya seemed perfect when I first put it on. But it can get to you after a while if you listen to it too long."

"Yeah, especially in the mood I'm in," I agreed, allowing a small smile.

"Have you heard Yanni's latest tape?"

"No. I don't know who Yanni is," I confessed.

"Then you've got to listen to this," Stan said, cutting Enya off mid-chant and quickly replacing it with another tape. Glistening piano spilled into my ears, the upbeat heart to the music transforming the sense of the room and, ever so slightly, my own foul mood.

"Ah," I agreed, nodding my head slightly, "that's great." Moving in front of the counter, I bent to the floor in a deep knee bend to look at the marked down calendars stacked on a low wooden table underneath the jewelry counter. I was glad Stan had changed the music, and I was inclined to buy myself a Yanni tape as a birthday treat, but I didn't want to talk anymore. Flicking through the several calendars stacked together, I suddenly came upon one with a wolf on *its* cover. I grunted and stood up to look elsewhere.

It was as if the book was sending out some unseen signal that called to me relentlessly. I couldn't get it out of my head. No matter where I went in the small store, it seemed as though I could see the title's bright, red-lettered "Wolf" out of the corner of my eye. Reluctantly, yet irresistibly, I returned to the culprit. I stood in front of the bookshelf on which it perched, the eyes of the wolf staring straight out at me, and read the title to myself again. Evil in everyday life? Ugh! But I took the book into my hands again and turned it over.

The back cover consisted of a warning, a warning that grated on me instantly. It spoke of the tendency in today's world to take a 'pollyanna' attitude toward the existence of evil, and the danger inherent in such a practice. *Well*, I thought to myself, *I recognize that evil exists. I've learned from all my reading that there cannot be 'light' without 'dark.'* 'Have you really learned that?' a small voice inside me dared to ask. *Of course I have!* I answered hastily. *I'm no pollyanna!* But as I stood there being confronted by myself, I had to admit that I also believed, deep in my heart, that if I didn't *think* about evil, if I didn't give it any credence or have 'evil' thoughts, I wouldn't have to worry about it. If I ignored evil, it wouldn't bother me. And I wanted to keep it that way.

The 'pollyanna' comment struck a nerve. Maybe I was being too cavalier in my approach toward the dark side. I randomly opened the book and immediately focussed on a single sentence two-thirds of the way through the first paragraph of Chapter Five. It jumped out at me and I knew instantly, without a doubt, that I'd come to this bookstore, this day, to buy this book.

It simply said: *"Know yourself."*

CHAPTER TWENTY SEVEN

Although my eyes skimmed the other words on the page, my brain failed to register any of them—a fact that would prove interesting when I finally did read the book. Instead, I quietly closed it, holding it firmly between my two hands, feeling the smooth, cool shine of the cover. *Know myself, know myself, know myself.* The words echoed hollowly through my mind over and over again. *Shit! Why do I keep getting this message?* I could practically see the Taos Indian standing in front of me again, repeating those words, this strange, simple message.

Well, maybe this book has something to teach me. I can't say that the subject matter appeals to me, but maybe that's not the point. 'Then again,' my inner voice interrupted, dripping with irony, 'maybe that *is* the point.'

As soon as I made the decision to buy the book, I knew it was time to leave. Approaching the counter, I interrupted Stan's reading. "I'll take that Yanni tape, too." Tentatively, half wishing the book would just disappear, I placed *Shouting at the Wolf* before me so Stan could write up the sale. Please don't talk to me about this, I thought silently.

"This is a new book," Stan said casually as he wrote the title out by hand in his receipt book. "You'll have to let me know how it is."

"Yeah, I will," I said quietly, my heart thumping in my ears.

"The book seemed to jump out at me as soon as I walked in the door!"

Stan looked up at me as he nodded sympathetically. "It's weird when that happens."

"I think so too. But the feeling's too clear," I sighed, shrugging my shoulders. "I'm supposed to read this book. I figure I better not ignore it."

Where now? I asked myself as I buckled my seatbelt. *Cuttalossa,* came the answer almost instantly. I'd been thinking about going there off and on all day. In fact, that's where I'd imagined myself walking and being in nature when I'd originally planned to spend my birthday outdoors.

But my birthday sure wasn't turning out the way I'd expected. As my car crossed over the canal bridge and I left New Hope behind me, the cloud of misery that had been my companion all day rejoined me, making me question every move I made. *I could go home instead of traipsing off to some cold, damp pity party of my own,* I thought, *and I know Karl is expecting to spend at least part of the day with me.*

No. I still didn't want to be with anyone. I needed to be quiet, to go within. Somehow, someway, I needed to make some sense out of the jumbled mush of thought and emotions cluttering my mind. On again, off again. Home, avoid home.

Turning off River Road and onto Cuttalossa, I could hear and feel the gravel under my wheels as the macadam turned to dirt a couple hundred yards in from the main road. To my left, I could see the Cuttalossa Creek cascading in a dramatic waterfall as it completed its rain-swelled journey to the Delaware River. Huge boulders lined the creek bed, and on the far side the ground sloped upward, sharply ending in a ridge that gently curved to the right and disappeared around the corner. On both sides of the narrow road, gnarled oaks and tall, straight hickory trees stood stark and naked in the forest, their leaves covering the floor of earth around them. Massive clumps of rhododendron, with leaves of such deep, dark green they merged almost seamlessly with the black shadows around them, jutted out from the sides of the hill. Shaggy clumps of moss clung to the faces of rocks haphazardly exposed on the hillsides, and forest ferns hunched protectively over the fallen oak and hickory leaves like guardian tarantulas.

I knew that just ahead, not more than a mile from here, a magical place exists that seems timeless and ethereal. Sheep with deep-toned bells around their necks graze placidly beside a pond surrounded by an eclectic mix of hens and roosters of several exotic breeds. A springhouse made of fieldstone, with a functioning wooden paddle wheel, overlooks a field where towering sycamores lean their massive trunks across thick, lush grasses. I'd driven past this magical place once or twice over the years and had vowed to come alone sometime as a gift to myself.

But the sun had been shining those other times. And the one lane bridge that transports visitors to this paradise had been open.

This time, though, an ugly faded white sign with chipped black lettering stood starkly at the beginning of the unpaved portion of the road. "ROAD CLOSED. BRIDGE OUT AHEAD." By its bedraggled appearance, the sign appeared to have been posted for years, although I knew that wasn't the case. It struck me as a most unfriendly sign; despite the written words, it felt to me as though it was actually saying, "GET OUT." Stubbornly reacting on a gut level to this rejection, which I took as a personal slight, I forged ahead anyway. As I allowed my car to creep slowly along the dirt road, my foot barely touching the accelerator, I pressed the button on the armrest beside me and a burst of cold, moist air filled my nostrils as the window opened. The smell of rotting leaves rode the roar of the creek's voice as both swirled into the car, chilling me quickly.

Eeeew, yuck, I thought, *what am I doing here?* Nothing was as I remembered it. Nothing looked even remotely as beautiful as I knew it to be. Puzzled, annoyed, I pulled over and parked the car against the side of a hill that steeply banked the road. My passenger side tires rested on layers of compacted leaves while my driver's side straddled the edge of the roadway.

Glancing at the brown paper bag sitting on the passenger seat, I rolled my eyes and regretted having purchased that stupid book and tape. Determined to spend some time with myself at the idyllic spot I knew lay ahead, I stepped out of the car onto the muddy road, glad I'd worn my hiking boots. Slamming the door, I briefly considered locking it, as is my habit. Then I glanced around at the trees and bushes and gloomy, overcast sky and had to laugh at myself. "The road is closed, for God's sake!" I said out loud, my voice echoing unnaturally in the wet environment. "No one's going to steal the car," I continued in a mumble. *No one but you is odd enough to even be taking a walk on a day like this.*

I looked through the rear window and noticed my journal laying upside down on the back seat, a pen clipped to the inside of its metal spiral binder. I wanted to write. Deep down inside I knew that I needed to sort out, on paper, all these awful feelings. But I wanted to write on my terms. I wanted to sit on a boulder in the sun, beside a gurgling brook, feeding well-groomed sheep that stayed only as long as they were invited. And I wanted answers to spring forth, clear and unequivocal, from my writing.

"Fat chance of that, " I growled angrily, abruptly deciding that I didn't need to write. "Bag that stupid-ass journal. Why do I even bother with it?"

I suddenly felt a strange sensation course through my body, not unlike the semi-nauseous buzz that occurs when I've had too much coffee on an empty stomach. I felt miserable, knotted and twisted up inside. Disgusted with myself, I dismissed any thoughts of bringing my journal and began walking up the middle of the road, looking for a place to sit and stare at the creek.

All I could hear was the water rushing along its course toward the Delaware. The roar made by its rapid flow over the rocks and boulders in its path bounced off the trees in the forest and echoed throughout the tiny valley between the cliffs. No birds sang. Were they wet? Cold? Why was the forest so silent and forbidding? Where was the peace I was seeking?

Inexplicably, rage filled every cell in my body as I stomped toward the creek. I wanted a better look at the water so I could pick a spot to sit at and calm myself. *The water is talking,* I heard myself think between the cracks of my spiky, foul mood. *Maybe I need to listen to it for some answers, for some guidance out of this stinking hole I'm in.* I wanted to believe I was listening. I wanted to believe that there is consciousness in everything—from rocks to trees to animals and people. I wanted to believe that if I asked for help I'd receive it. And I wanted to believe I was close to discovering my way, my path.

Bullshit! screamed my ego. *This is all a waste of time! You're not going to get any guidance. You might as well just turn around and go home. There are no answers. Just do what you're told and make the best out of your miserable life.*

Suddenly, it all became clear. My ego was right. I was a fool. I believed in a magical side of life that simply did not exist. I'd been duped—by myself, by Catherine, by all the books I'd read. But most of all I'd been duped by my own soul, by that part of me deep down inside that insisted my life had a grander purpose, a deeper meaning than anything as simple as how much education I had or how I earned my money. The vast futility and foolishness of my quest for meaning and answers and guidance overcame me in a gust of despair.

The sound of branches crackling made me look up, across the creek, to the crest of the ridge opposite me where three dark figures stood, watching. As I tried to focus my eyes on them, they ran a few yards to the right, then disappeared into the thick, dark jumble of evergreen branches and rhododendron.

"That's right!" I screamed. "It's all shit! All the stuff I've learned has been bogus, bullshit, idealistic pap!" Angrily, I kicked a small stone toward the creek and it skipped and pinged off two different rocks before landing in the water. Fury swept around me like a dust devil and grabbed me by the throat.

"Fuck all of it!" I shouted to the rocks and the trees. "The teachings, the studies, the metaphysical 'truths.'" I laughed bitterly and realized I was crying. "There's no one out there! There's no Great Mystery! It's all a bunch of shit!" Bitter tears of anguish and frustration streamed down my face.

Self-indulgent, petulant tears, a small voice whispered in the back of my mind.

"Shut up!" I yelled out loud. "I've had enough of you! I've *tried* to listen and follow my intuition. I've *tried* to live my life with integrity and purpose. And all I get are cases I hate and clients who cheat me!" I sobbed, only faintly aware of my gross generalization. "I want to feel alive! I want to feel good about what I do. Is that too much to ask?"

My words echoed off the craggy outcroppings and were swallowed by cold, gray silence. Not even the water of the creek, mindlessly rushing to its own destiny, bothered to respond.

I was alone.

CHAPTER TWENTY EIGHT

Across from my car, the bed of the creek lay only a foot or so lower than the roadway. This is no good, I thought to myself. Feeling an inexplicable urge to perch high above the water and listen deeply to its voice as it crashed over rocks, I knew I needed a better vantage point from which to watch and listen, even if it was only watching and listening to my own angry thoughts.

Fishing in my jacket pocket for a tissue, I found one and wiped away the tears that had pooled under my chin. I blew my nose and carefully folded the tissue, returning it to my pocket. Unconsciously, I fingered my car keys.

I trudged up the side of the creek, walking across the brown weeds that had been packed flat against the earth by the snow we'd had only a few weeks ago. I was silent now, no longer bothering to hurl my anger into the air around me. I felt ashamed of my outburst. As angry and frustrated as I was at my apparent lack of clarity, I didn't want to give up. I didn't want to stop my search for meaning.

I need a nice big boulder to sit on. Peering up the bed of the creek, I tried to locate the source of the rushing turbulence ahead. I could hear a loud roar coming from further up the creek, as if from a waterfall. Sure enough, about three hundred yards ahead, the creek hurtled past a moss-covered wall of fitted stone imbedded in the cliff opposite me. The wall had an ancient appearance and I wondered, briefly, who could have built it and why. As I made my way toward the noise, I noticed that here the bank of the creek rose dramatically above its bed. There were two tiers, actually. The roadway to my right, obviously going up an incline, snaked its way toward the bridge being repaired about a half mile ahead. I carefully picked my way around scattered rocks and forest undergrowth as I followed the creek to my left. The creek angled sharply to the right just after the stone wall and about five yards further I discovered a small waterfall. Water flowing rapidly over a flat stone precipice clattered noisily from stone to stone, haphazardly splashing over, against and under a massive chunk of tree limb, naked of bark, which had caught its base in the boulders beneath the precipice and was sticking two pale jagged arms up into the cascade.

Cool, dank air engulfed my face as I stepped toward the edge above the creek. My ears could feel the pressure of the roiling water as it struggled to flow past the obstructions in its path. The clatter was magnified as it echoed off the steep, sheer rock face of the opposite bank.

Mist rising from the turbulent water left the rock wall on the opposite bank wet and black with moisture. "Yes," I said softly to this dark, angry place. "You know how I feel."

The perfect boulder was before me. Four feet long and roughly three feet across, it had plenty of room on it for me to sit cross-legged and, since it was lodged some ten feet above the surface of the creek, it afforded me the view I'd been searching for. As I approached the boulder I noticed that it had lain there a long time. Weeds grew up and around it and moss and lichens of gray, brown and green gave the massive stone a splotched, mottled hue. I tentatively placed my right foot on its face. Drawing my left foot up, I stepped onto the rock intending to lower myself down cross-legged.

I stood on the rock, straight up, for the briefest of moments. As I reached my full height, everything around me instantly began swirling before my eyes. Without having a chance to even form words in my mind, I scrambled to grasp what was happening.

The world whirled before me and I became aware of a deep rumbling from behind and underneath me. The grinding, sickening, scraping sound of rock against rock filled me. Was I hearing it, feeling it, or just *knowing* it? *OH MY GOD! I'm falling!* my voice shrieked inside my head as I looked at my feet and saw the nightmare unfolding before my eyes. The boulder had broken away from the edge of the bank and I was being hurled, face first, toward the seething water below, teeming with craggy rocks and debris. There was nowhere for me to reach, nothing to hold onto. Instinctively, I tried to thrust myself from the boulder toward the bank on my left, slightly downstream, but the rock falling out from under my feet afforded little leverage. The boulder was already crashing toward the center of the creek as my body twisted in a futile effort to save itself. As I flew through the air and helplessly watched my body use every instinctive maneuver to save itself, all I could think was, *This is bad. I could die.* Then I smashed, face first and flat-bodied, into the rocks at creek's edge.

Pain. Shooting, searing, intense pain . . . everywhere. *Get out of the water! Get out of the water!* The words shrieked repeatedly over and over and over in my head. I could think nothing else. Nothing else mattered. To survive, I knew I had to get myself out before the magnitude of this crisis could even begin to sink in. I could not think. I didn't know why I had to get out of the water; all I could hear was the intense necessity conveyed by the voice in my head.

Desperately, I struggled to my knees and dragged myself toward the mud and grass above the water line. *Get out, get out, get out, get out!* kept running through my head in a strange sort of survival mantra. Once out of the water, I knew I had to get up to the road, somehow, someway. It was a miracle that I'd survived the fall. Now I had to get to my car.

My body was beginning to buzz. Only faintly aware that I was soaked and starting to feel cold, I again labored to my knees and tried to raise myself up onto my feet. My right leg buckled as soon as I placed any weight on it. "Oh no, " I groaned out loud, beginning to realize that my ordeal wasn't over. Looking up, I was overwhelmed by the distance and height I had to climb. I tried again, only this time babying my leg—my ankle, I suspected was the problem, although it was hard to identify the specific damage I'd sustained.

No go. I couldn't place any weight on it at all.

Suddenly, my awareness shifted to my mouth, which, I realized, was filled with blood. I could feel gravel on my tongue and I spat it out into the weeds. Mixed in with the bright crimson blood were several small black and gray pieces of gravel—and a conspicuously white piece of material which was, to my dismay, a jagged piece of one of my teeth. My tongue searched for the source of this loss and located it immediately. An incisor was slashed with part of it lost to the gum line. The tooth beside that one felt raw and partially crushed.

"Ohhhh," a terrified, guttural moan issued involuntarily from the deepest part of my being as I felt my mouth again begin to fill with blood. The iron taste made me ill. My arms and chest started to shake uncontrollably and with a faint whooshing sound, like the crackle of static electricity, the grass around me faded to variations of black and gray.

"Don't panic," I said out loud in a quavering voice, surprised at how far away it sounded. The buzzing in my head and body threatened to engulf me. "It's OK, it's OK," I tried to reassure myself, but the words sounded almost too faint to be mine. I closed my eyes and deliberately focused my attention inward. I drew a deep breath inside my lungs and tried to hold it, but lost it in a fit of coughing. I tried again. The dimming of my world had shot a course of terror through my heart. I struggled to stay conscious.

Lifting my head, still on my hands and knees, I peered up toward the road. I couldn't see its surface, but a tall, straight oak, towering ahead of me, marked the road's edge and gave me a destination to work toward. Slowly, painfully, I dragged myself to the tree, realizing along the way that my left hand was of as much use to me as my right foot.

The light in the hollow was growing dimmer than before and the mist thick. Crawling to the cadence of my own soft moaning, an odd composite of a comforting croon and a terrified cry, I reached the base of the smooth-barked tree and leaned my back against its trunk, allowing myself a moment to rest and consider my next move. As I clumsily tried to position myself so I could sit on my bottom, an unexpected bolt of pain seared through my lower spine triggering yet another brownout of my awareness.

"Oh my God, what have I done?" I choked out in a cry. I felt paralyzed by fear that another movement would send me into unconsciousness, yet I knew the growing darkness and my cold, wet clothes could render the same result. I had no choice. I must get to the car, and I had to crawl the distance. Gathering my spring jacket about me, which I'd realized when I first got out of the car was a poor choice for the day, I searched again for the comforting touch of my keys. Not feeling them immediately, or more disconcerting, not hearing their familiar clink-clink at my touch, I frantically burrowed underneath the wad of damp tissues and felt only the seam of the pocket. No keys.

A wave of nausea and panic washed through me and I leaned to my right, spit out more blood, and struggled to raise myself up on my right hand and knee enough to effect a makeshift head-between-my-knees effort at staying conscious. "Now what do I do?" I asked the gravel between my hands.

Gently easing myself back into a sitting position, I closed my eyes, pulled my jacket tightly around myself, and considered my options. *Here I am, on a closed dirt road, just before twilight on Good Friday. No one knows where I am. I've fallen, face-first, into a rocky creek bed. I've broken teeth, I'm bleeding, and I'm freezing cold and wet. I can't bear weight on my right foot, or grasp anything with my left hand, and it feels like my ass is broken as well.*

WEIK

And now my only chance to save myself is lost because my keys are halfway to the Delaware River.

The gravity of my situation hit me with stark clarity, yet with that clarity came an unexpected sense of peace. I knew, with a sudden strange certainty, that somehow I would survive. I couldn't do it alone. I had to ask for help. Hardest of all, though, I had to *trust* that it would come.

CHAPTER TWENTY NINE

"Help!" I yelled out, my shoulders pressing uncomfortably against the firm support of the oak. "Helloooo," I howled, aiming my mouth toward the treetops, "I need help here! Helloooo!"

I've been reduced to this, I thought to myself. *This is pathetic. What are the chances of anyone hearing me?*

Be patient. Surrender.

What choice did I have? "Helloooo! Help! Can anyone hear me?" I tried again, feeling silly despite my injuries. My words felt like frightened finches, fluttering up into the naked branches high above me, leaving me to sit helplessly propped against a tree in the middle of nowhere. The roar of the creek, coming from behind and below me, was all I could hear, its raw voice mocking me and stealing the paltry warmth both my body and spirit were trying desperately to conserve.

Suddenly I heard some sharp, leafy crashes to my left. A squirrel?

There it was again. It sounded bigger than a squirrel. A dog? The sound was coming from around the bend, up the creek, toward the bridge that was out. Unbidden, a rancid little thought poked its way into my head asking me just what would I do if somebody awful came upon me. Somebody from whom I couldn't escape because of my injuries?

Trust.

"No, no. Shut up!" someone whispered insistently from the same direction as the crashing leaves. I could barely make the words out. Was this wishful thinking?

"Hello?" I called out again. "Please! I need help here!"

"See? I told you!" a man's voice rang out triumphantly. In a clatter of boots and leaves and gravel, two men and a woman rounded the corner and rushed toward me. Gently, they lifted me off my side, where I'd drifted, and back up into more of a sitting position.

"What happened, honey?" asked the woman, whom I later found out was named Karen.

Shaking with relief and cold, I tried to explain but found that my mouth was having a hard time forming the words. "I . . . fell," I said, my teeth chattering hard, "into . . . the creek."

"You've got to be kidding!" she said, looking up at her two companions with a grimace of disbelief. "How long have you been here?"

"I don't know," I admitted. "A . . . little bit."

"Can you walk?"

"No. I'm pretty hurt . . . all over, kind of . . . ." I shifted my weight and cried out as a flame shot from my tailbone straight up my spine.

"She's in shock," I heard one of the guys say.

How can I be in shock if I can hear and understand what they're saying?

"I'm going to run back and see if I can get a blanket," said the same man who'd assessed my condition. "Should I call an ambulance?"

"No ambulance," I stated emphatically. God, that's all I needed.

"Well how are we going to get you some help?" asked Karen gently. "Our truck is on the other side of the bridge, up the road," she said, gesturing with her thumb. "But the bridge is out, so we can't even drive over here to get you warm or take you to a hospital."

"My husband. He's home. He'll come to get me." I begged Karen with my eyes. "Would you at least try to see if he's home before you call an ambulance?"

"What's your number?" asked the taller of the two men, the one who wanted to get me a blanket. "I'll find a phone and get something to keep you warm," he said as he walked over and squatted on one knee beside me, bringing his face to my eye level. I gave him my number and he wrote it down on the back of a receipt that he pulled from his pocket. "You're gonna be OK now, all right?" he confirmed for both of us, his striking blue eyes searching my face. Before I could answer, he jumped to his feet and took off.

Karen laughed and shook her head as we listened to him run up the road. "I think he feels responsible for you."

"Why?" I asked, surprised.

"Because he heard you calling for help a while ago and we didn't believe him."

"Oh," I said, trying to smile but realizing that my lips were stiff with caked blood. "How did you get here?" asked Karen suddenly. She stood up and squinted down the road toward my car, which was barely visible between its black color, the waning light, and the generally murky atmosphere. "Is that your car?"

"Yeah," I said, "but I lost my keys when I fell."

"Oh no!"

"Yup," I said, nodding my head slightly. "I didn't realize it until I'd crawled all the way up here from the creek." I struggled to swallow. "That's when I started calling for help."

"Jack!" Karen yelled to the third member of my rescue trio. I'd completely lost track of him—forgotten him, really, in the excitement of talking to the other two. "Come 'ere!" she called.

Crash, crash, crash, I could hear him approach as he bounded through the leaves behind me. Before Karen could say anything else to him, Jack rounded the tree and looked me in the face.

"Did you fall right back there?" he asked, pointing behind me and slightly up the creek toward the bridge.

"Yeah, I think so," I answered hesitantly. I wasn't completely certain because I'd lost my bearings somewhat when I'd slammed into the rocks. "Near the waterfall," I added. "I was going to sit and look at it."

"Holy *shit*," exclaimed Jack unexpectedly. "I thought so. There's a boulder down there in the creek that looks like it just rolled in. But the gash in the earth where it obviously came from is, like, ten or twelve feet above the creek!"

Nauseous terror washed over me as his words verified the enormity of my accident.

"She lost her keys when she fell," interrupted Karen, almost as if she didn't want to hear Jack's proclamation. "Would you go down and see if you can find them?"

"That's hopeless," I groaned, returning my attention to the problem at hand.

"Maybe not. It's worth a try," Jack agreed. Turning to Karen, he said in a more subdued voice, "You've gotta come and see this."

"I will in a minute," Karen agreed. "I don't want to leave Lisa right now," she said smiling at me. I didn't remember telling her my name, but I guessed I had when I'd given them my telephone number. "She needs to get warm!"

Jack made his way back down to the creek and Karen sank down beside me. "I'm sorry I don't have a jacket or anything to give you," she said apologetically. I looked at her mustard colored coveralls as she turned toward me, reached for my shoulders, and gently tried to adjust my lean against the tree.

"That's OK," I said, again making an effort to smile. "How could you have known you'd be on a rescue mission today?"

"On days like this I usually wear a couple of layers of thermal underwear under my coveralls," she continued. "It's easier than messing with a jacket." She looked at me and took my cold, clammy hands into her own. "But that doesn't do you much good, does it? Can I do anything to make you more comfortable?"

"No, I don't think so. I'm OK if I don't move. But—aaack!" I yelped as I made an effort to shift my weight slightly. Reflexively, I put my left hand out to steady myself and cried out in pain as soon as it touched the gravel beside me, forgetting that my hand was also cut, bruised and swelling. When I retracted it, my bottom moved and searing pain again shot up my spine. "Oh, oh," was all I could manage to say.

"You know, it's kind of a miracle that we found you," Karen said softly as I held myself very still, trying to calm my throbbing body. Her words sifted slowly into my consciousness as I struggled to keep from passing out.

"Why? What do you mean?"

"Well, we were up the creek, around the bend here," she began, gesturing with her right hand, which looked rough from working in the elements, "about half a mile up the road. Peter was about thirty feet in the air, topping off a tree, when he yelled down to us that he thought he could hear someone calling for help." Karen laughed quietly, almost to herself. "Neither Jack nor I had heard anything and we were on ground level, so we told him he was imagining things." Karen stood up, dusted off the bottom of her coveralls and turned to face me, squatting down to my eye level. Absently, she gathered up some pebbles from the small mound running along the berm and let them sift through her fingers into the palm of her other hand. "A few minutes went by, and I was trying to pay attention to see if I could hear anything, but I didn't hear a thing that sounded like someone crying for help. Then Peter said he heard it again, only this time he was more insistent. That's when Jack and I started to tease him unmercifully because, well . . . ." she hesitated, "because Peter is almost completely deaf."

"Huh?" I exclaimed, a strange feeling fluttering in the pit of my stomach.

"Yeah," she said, nodding her head. "He's deaf in one ear

and, quite frankly, has a tough time hearing us with his good ear—particularly when he's working high up in a tree." She stood up abruptly and once again wiped her hands on her coveralls. "So we teased him and told him he was hearing the voices of wood fairies," she laughed a little sheepishly. "But he became agitated, which isn't like him, and insisted upon coming out of the tree and walking down the road here—which is how we found you."

Just then, a voice called from what sounded like the bridge. "I'm coming!" the voice called out to us. It was Peter.

The two of them swaddled me in the thin, pale yellow blanket Peter brought and, even though it wasn't all that soft or cuddly, it did cushion my back against the oak and provided some insulation against the chill air. "Thank you so much," I said to them gratefully.

"No problem," Peter answered easily. "Your husband should be here soon—at least he said he'd be here in ten minutes," he continued, concern creasing his Scandinavian features.

"What did you tell him?" I asked, feeling guilty that I was putting Karl through such a scare.

"Just that you'd fallen and hurt yourself and that you didn't want us to call an ambulance."

I groaned. Poor Karl. He must have flipped when he'd heard that they wanted to call an ambulance.

"Don't worry," Peter added, as if I'd expressed my guilt out loud. "I told him that you're OK."

Suddenly, a whoop came from down by the bank of the creek, where Karen had gone to help Jack in his search. "I found them! Whew-hoo!" hollered Jack triumphantly. I could vaguely hear the familiar jingle of my keys as he bounded up the hill. "I'll go get the car and we'll get you warm in no time," he said as he came up behind me. "Which key?" he asked, thrusting them before me. I showed him the two Oldsmobile keys and he took off down the road.

"Lisa?" Karen's voice called up from the creek. "Were you wearing glasses when you fell?"

"No . . . ." I said uncertainly as I tried to remember for sure. I struggled to recall, but that detail was too fuzzy to remember accurately.

The crackling leaves heralded Karen's approach. "Are these yours?" she asked, holding out a pair of deep blue frames with one lens popped out.

"Yup, those are mine. I can't believe they're not broken!" I said, marveling at my incredible luck with the keys and the glasses.

"What's even weirder is that I found this," Karen whisked her other hand from behind her back, proudly displaying the missing lens.

"Oh my God!" Peter and I exclaimed together.

"Yeah, my thought exactly," Karen remarked. "I found the glasses and was turning to come up here when a twinkle of light caught my eye just as I was stepping out of the water—and it was your lens." Looking over her shoulder toward the west, up the creek, where the sun had already set, she added, "I don't know where the glint of light came from, though." With a wistful smile, she turned back toward us and shrugged her shoulders.

At that moment, Jack pulled the car up to within a yard of where I was sitting, and Peter and Karen supported me as I eased myself into the driver's seat. It seemed as if the engine had barely warmed up when Karl arrived to take me to the hospital.

After five hours of x-rays and tests for internal injuries, the emergency room staff discharged me in disbelief. Other than my teeth, not one bone was broken nor did I need even one stitch.

"It's a miracle you weren't killed—either by the fall or by exposure," I heard more than once. "But no broken bones?" They shook their heads.

"I know," I agreed, the stark lights and efficient sterility of the emergency room making my afternoon's experience seem even further from reality. "It's hard to believe any of this is real."

I never saw Peter, Karen, or Jack ever again. But the funny thing is, Karl swears I was alone when he arrived and that he never had a chance to personally thank the man who called to tell him that I'd fallen into the creek. Yet I remember waving goodbye to them from the window of Karl's car—at least, I *think* I do.

CHAPTER THIRTY

"Oh my God!" my mother exclaimed as she opened the glass-paned wooden door leading into my parents' kitchen. "What did you do to yourself?" she asked me, worry etched into every cell of her face as she unsuccessfully tried to hug me without causing additional pain. "You look like you've been in a horrible car accident!" she exclaimed.

My father stood behind her a few feet, watching me without expression as I slowly negotiated my way up the two stone steps from the driveway onto the flagstone porch. The hospital staff had insisted that I take a cane when they discharged me the night before, but I was having difficulty maintaining my balance with it. Karl was at my side, trying to help me walk but not really able to do anything for me since there was nowhere on my body that he could hold to steady me without making me wince in pain. Not quite twenty-four hours had transpired since my plunge into the creek.

"You can kith me here," I said to my mom as I presented her with my swollen right cheek. "It'th thtill numb." I gave her a smile with my eyes, but mirrored in our faces was our mutual horror at my condition.

Karl had just picked me up from my dentist's office, where she had performed some emergency work on my mouth. Although I was scheduled for more procedures in a few days, she had put a temporary crown on the broken tooth and filed some of the splintering of the other teeth so that I could at least attempt to eat without causing more damage. I'd also bitten my tongue and the inside of my right cheek had a nasty laceration.

While I was being assessed at the emergency room the night before, Karl had run the boys up to stay with Mom and Dad. Now we were here to retrieve our sons and celebrate my birthday as Karl and Mom had planned for the evening of my accident. My 'performance,' as both Karl and my mother liked to term it, had scratched those plans and they reminded me of that fact every chance they could get.

As we walked into the kitchen, Daniel and Max came running out to greet us. "Happy birthday Mommy!" shouted Max happily, oblivious to my battered condition in his three-year-old exuberance.

"Hi bunny, " I replied, trying to smile as best as I could through the Novocaine in my cheeks. I tried hard not to wince as Max planted a kiss on my lips and threw his arms around my neck. "Be careful!" I cautioned through clenched teeth as I tried to maintain my smile, "Mommy's got some boo boos."

"Where were you?" Max accused me, backing up to get a better look into my eyes. "I missed you," he said, his sky blue eyes swallowing me whole.

I nearly lost all this, I thought suddenly, my breath catching in my throat.

"Hi Mom," interrupted Daniel, his voice and expression much more subdued than his little brother's. "Happy birthday." His eyes searched mine and, after taking in my puffy, bruised face, landed on the cane that I was holding in my right hand. "What *happened* to you?" he asked, his voice aghast.

"I'm OK," I lied. "I fell yesterday when I was taking a walk in the woods, and I hurt my foot." His eyes followed my gaze to my right foot, which was fat with swelling and an ace bandage, and was covered with a thick purple wool sock.

"Is it broken?" my father asked, the first words he'd uttered since my slow and awkward entrance. He knew it wasn't. We'd called when we got home last night to let them know the results of all the testing.

"Nope, nope," I reassured everyone. "Nothing's broken. I'm just very banged and bruised." I looked toward the marble-topped, wrought iron kitchen table, and the two sets of matching wrought iron chairs flanking it. I needed to sit down before I fell down.

Deftly saving me, my mother announced, "I think it's only right, since it's your birthday and you're obviously not going to be any help in getting dinner," she teased, "that you should sit in my seat so you can put your foot up and watch us all scurry around to wait on you."

"OK," I said simply, starting to feel overwhelmed and a little bit woozy.

"That wasn't a hard sell," commented my father dryly. Sympathy and compassion never were his strong suits.

As I set my sights on the chair wedged into the corner between the near side of the kitchen table and the window, Karl disappeared into the next room and returned carrying one of the wooden dining room chairs, its seat a tapestry of needlepoint hand-stitched by my grandmother. My father turned his attention to the filet mignon that he was preparing and Mom turned the oven on to preheat it for the baked potatoes. Moving ever so slowly, I eased myself down onto the quilted cushion tied to the seat of the wrought iron chair. Grimacing but silent, I tried to find a comfortable position. Lost in an inward focus of locating an area on my body that didn't hurt, I opened my eyes to see my mother staring at me in concern, a fistful of silverware clutched in her right hand, cloth placemats in the other.

The look on my mother's face wrenched my heart. I hadn't meant for her to see the extent of my pain. Mommy was the one who needed us to focus on her health which, little by little seemed only to be getting worse, much as she tried to pretend otherwise. I felt ashamed.

"Baby," she said softly as she sank onto the chair Karl had just placed at the head of the table. Gently she placed her left hand over my throbbing foot, which I'd propped temporarily on the seat between us. "How in the world did this happen?"

I recounted the specifics of my fall, leaving out the vehement anger I'd spewed at the Universe. My parents didn't need to know of my utter despair, that I feared my calls for guidance were being ignored, or that I'd scoffed at my belief that everything is connected. I didn't think they'd understand since, in their eyes, I had the world by the tail. A great husband, two healthy, happy sons, and a career that made them beam with pride. My yearning for something beyond those externals would be met by misunderstanding at the very least and, quite possibly, ridicule.

"Well what the hell were you doing that for?" demanded my father when he heard I'd decided to take a walk by myself in the woods.

"Because I like to be in nature," I answered him wearily, glad that I'd spared him the details of my internal conflict.

"Seems like a pretty *stupid* thing to do."

I cringed inside but tried not to show how sharply his opinion stung. I could feel my face getting hot and I looked to Karl for help.

"We take a lot of walks," offered Karl.

"Well if you do it so often you'd think you'd be better at it," my father countered, looking at me with disdain. "You mean to tell me that you didn't notice that the boulder was about to fall in the creek?" He glared at me with a look that demanded an explanation I didn't have.

I shrugged my shoulders. "I know, Daddy, it's strange," I tried to explain, swallowing my desire to scream at him for being so judgmental and insensitive. "It's not as if I've never taken a walk in the woods or climbed on rocks before. You know that! And I was careful," I said, pausing as I momentarily relived the awful sensation of having the earth spin toward me, out of control. In my mind's eye I could picture how the boulder looked when I approached it. "It seemed so solidly anchored, as if it had been there for hundreds of years," I mused out loud. "Even when it started to roll, my mind didn't consider the rock coming loose as an option. I couldn't comprehend what was happening."

My father simply pressed his lips together and shook his head. "Well I hope you learned your lesson," he muttered. "You shouldn't have been there in the first place."

I bristled and started to respond when my mother interjected, "I'm just relieved that you didn't break any bones . . . or worse."

"Yeah, me too," Karl agreed with Mom, complicit in her attempt to ward off an argument between my father and me. "They couldn't believe it at the emergency room when nothing showed up broken. And they couldn't figure out how she must have twisted and landed, since she hurt so many different areas of her body: her face and teeth, her left hand, right elbow, right foot and lower back," he said, ticking off the list for my parents. "Front, back, left, and right!" Karl leaned across the table toward me and patted my right hand. "When you go jumping off cliffs you don't mess around."

"But I didn't jump," I said quietly. I felt like I'd been pushed—or thrown—but I certainly didn't want to admit that, especially as I sat here defending myself at my parents' kitchen table. The whole incident was taking on a surreal quality. I'd been taught a lesson yesterday, but I was pretty sure it wasn't the one my father had in mind.

CHAPTER THIRTY ONE

I ate very little of my birthday dinner since the Novocaine numb was soon replaced by literal in-my-face pain, but by everyone else's account it was delicious. We returned home early in the evening because it was, after all, the night before Easter and preparations had to be made. Particularly since I'd broken no bones, I was determined that my injuries were not going to interfere with the rest of our lives

Yet coloring the eggs was a rote, joyless chore this year. There was something unsettling in the air, but I tried to tell myself it was just exhaustion from the turmoil of the past couple of days.

By the time the theme from the 11 o'clock news began blaring excitedly from the small television on our dresser, my rationalizations were falling apart. Karl had said few words to me on our ride home and virtually nothing since we'd put the boys to bed. In fact, as soon as he'd tucked them in, he climbed in on his side of our bed, pulled the covers up, and rolled over, away from me, his body a lump of silent anger.

I felt on the verge of despair. I couldn't move without hurting, yet Karl was deliberately shutting me out and leaving the Easter basket duties to me. The best I could muster was a half-sit, half-lean as I wearily tried to situate myself on the top of our quilt.

I sat there, staring at the Easter grass, candy, and assorted special goodies I'd gathered for the baskets days ago (and just retrieved from my bedroom closet with great difficulty) and allowed the tears welling in my eyes to trickle down my cheeks. For all the physical pain I was in, nothing matched the bereft loneliness and heartache that I felt at that moment. I'd had to crawl on my hands and knees to get up the stairs to our bedroom; how in the world was I ever going to get the baskets into the boys' rooms? Why was Karl rejecting me like this?

Through my tears I stared at his back, wondering how he could put on such a caring, loving front to my parents and then so effectively—and abruptly—cut me off from any contact with him. I hated his silence, his refusal to simply talk to me and tell me what he was feeling. As soon as we'd driven out of my parents' driveway I'd felt his attitude shift. When I'd asked him what was wrong, he'd replied with a curt, "Nothing," and pretended to focus his attention strictly on the road ahead of us. From then on all conversation, if you could call it that, had been veiled, through the boys, with a marked lack of eye contact.

I gasped in surprise, then, when his voice betrayed the fact that he was not asleep.

"You really scared me," he blurted, his blanketed form barely moving.

"What?" I croaked, hastily leaning toward my night table to grab a tissue and blow my nose. Relief gushed through me. At least he was willing to talk.

"You really scared me yesterday," he repeated, his back still facing me. His voice sounded angry and strained, as though it was physically hard for him to get the words out.

"I'm sorry," I replied automatically. Karl didn't answer. In the silence I noticed how hollow my apology sounded. Then I felt the tickle of annoyance at the back of my throat. "You act as if I did this on purpose," I said. "Is that it? Is that why you're not helping me with the Easter baskets?" I didn't give him a chance to respond. "Because you think I did this on purpose and so now you're going to punish me for it?!?"

Karl turned himself around under the covers so that he was facing me, his head propped up on his right arm. "I don't think you deliberately set out to do it," Karl conceded. "But I do think that you have more responsibility for it happening than you're admitting. At the very least—on the most superficial level—you weren't caring enough about yourself or us to keep yourself safe."

I thought about what he was saying for a moment. "Yeah, you're right," I began, but he cut me off.

"But there's a lot more to this, Lis," he continued. "My God, when I think about where you fell," he sounded like he was getting angry again. "Do you have any idea how lucky you are— we all are—that you weren't killed?" he demanded, his eyes flashing.

"I know," I admitted. "You're right." After a moment I added, "And it really was my fault. I was being totally disrespectful to the Universe."

"What do you mean?"

"You know how things were Friday morning," I began, "and how we haven't been getting along lately . . . ."

"Yeah."

"And you know how I've been asking for guidance and feel like all I'm getting is a test pattern in response?"

Karl smiled and nodded. We'd drawn that analogy frequently on our walks lately.

"Well, I got really frustrated on Friday, feeling like the more we learn and the more we try to live our lives in sync with this stuff, like trusting our intuition, and believing that everything happens for a reason, the worse off our lives seem to be getting."

"I know what you mean," Karl agreed, pulling himself up to a cross-legged position under the covers. "I've been feeling super frustrated lately too."

That's why you've been sneaking cigarettes, I thought to myself, but bit my tongue. I didn't want to start yet another angle of fighting tonight.

"And it seems like we have no one we can truly trust," I

continued. "Like this baloney that's going on with Beth and Catherine. It just seems so out of balance and . . . wrong somehow. Am I imagining that things are getting really weird with them? Why can't Catherine see what's going on in the name of her school and church? And does she fail to see it or is she, God forbid, condoning it? Or am I just jealous of their close relationship?"

"I don't think so, Lis," Karl interrupted. "Do you really want to be best friends with Catherine?"

I thought a moment. "No, I don't want to be her best friend. I just want her to teach us metaphysics and . . . I don't know."

"And what?"

"And not act in a way that makes me doubt her integrity," I confessed. "I hate it that she talks behind my back about me 'being the owl' and then doesn't even mention it when she sees me. And I hate it that she seems to be cultivating this relationship with Beth, who practically kisses the ground she walks on, without seeing that something fishy is going on. I want to respect Catherine—and I *do* respect her for her obvious knowledge and clairvoyant abilities. But, as she would say herself, something's not quite cooked about the way things are going now . . . and it makes me doubt everything I've been learning lately."

A commercial for peanut M& Ms filled our bedroom with its cutesy message as Karl and I sat in silence.

"So anyway," I continued, "when I went for my walk on Friday I was feeling lots of anger and frustration at every one and every thing and I started yelling at the rocks and the creek and all of Nature, really, saying that it was all shit. I shouted that all that we're learning is crap and that I was going to stop looking for messages in everything and stop trying to make sense out of my life and just go back to thinking about things the way I used to— and living a life with no sense of wonder because it's all bullshit anyway," I finished. Passion, frustration, and the ugly memory of Friday afternoon's emotions made my heart pound in my ears.

"Wow," Karl remarked. "And then you fell?"

"I walked up the creek a bit, and I'd even calmed down somewhat," I said. "But as soon as I stepped on that boulder it felt like the world started spinning up toward my face, more than me falling toward the earth. It was bizarre," I said with a shudder.

We sat for several moments, silently watching the images on the small TV screen dart hypnotically before our eyes.

"I couldn't think when I got the call," Karl said softly. "I just reacted. I just got in the car and tried not to think, because I didn't even want to imagine what life would be like for us if something awful happened to you." His voice sounded raw, wounded.

"I *am* sorry, Karl," I said earnestly, touching the back of his hand and then taking it in my own. Tears were streaming down my face and Karl's eyes were brimming as well. "You've been treating me, since we left Mom and Dad's, as though I deliberately set out to hurt myself or make life inconvenient for you and the boys. You've got to know how much that hurt!"

"I know. I was angry at you for being so careless with yourself."

"But I didn't do it on purpose!" I cried.

"I know that," he said quickly. "Especially now that I've heard the whole story of what happened." He was quiet for several moments and I could feel myself starting to run out of gas. "But now that I know the whole story," he continued, "I think I'm even more blown away than I was earlier."

"It was scary," I agreed. I thought a moment and corrected myself. "It *is* scary. I know I need to look at what happened with clear sight and deal with the fact that, somehow, I narrowly escaped death yesterday. I'm still struggling with the actual reality of that fact." I took a deep breath and held it, slowly letting the air escape from my lungs. "I know that my attitude played a huge part in what happened and that I'm being taught an enormous lesson. But I'm exhausted right now," I said, glancing at the nearly completed Easter baskets, "and I doubt that my clarity is at its best at the moment. Will you be a bunny and make the deliveries?"

"Sure," Karl said, squeezing my hand three times then letting it go.

"Thanks for talking to me," I said as I watched him get out of bed and come around to my side.

"I could hear you sniffling," he said, "and I knew you were hurting. I *wanted* you to feel bad," he admitted, looking me straight in the eyes. "But as I tried to ignore you I realized that I wouldn't be so angry if I didn't love you so much." Looking deeply into my eyes, he kissed me lightly on the lips. "And as much as I resisted it, I knew that if we didn't talk, things would never get better."

CHAPTER THIRTY TWO

"**M**mmy!" an urgent whisper breathed warm and wet in my ear. "Mommy, wake up! The Easter Bunny came!"

I smiled, my eyes not yet open, as I tried to separate dream from reality. Max, my three-year-old, had been in my dream, yet I knew now that his voice was coming from outside my body instead of from inside my head. I felt like I was coming up for air after taking a deep dive and that I had to reach a certain level before I could form the words of a response.

"He came to you too!" Max shouted with glee when he spotted the Easter basket beside my bed. "Ooooh, you got two nests!" he said with enthusiastic envy as he took a quick inventory of my basket and noticed the green chocolate birds' nests with jellybean eggs. "Mommy," he said again impatiently, tugging at my shoulder. "Wake up!"

"Yeah, wake up you guys," chimed in Daniel, whose voice gave away the fact that he was on the other side of the bed, checking out his father's basket. "Mmmm, peanut M&M's, Dad," he teased his father.

"Don't touch my basket," Karl threatened with a growl. Our bed lurched as Karl propped himself up and both boys jumped onto our covers with their baskets.

"Watch out!" I yelled reflexively as Max narrowly missed landing on my right foot, which I had elevated on a pillow. All the jostling made me acutely aware of how much my body hurt—everywhere—this morning. "Happy Easter, guys!" I said through gritted teeth as I struggled to sit upright. My rear end hurt even more than it had yesterday and my eyes welled up as I tried to find a comfortable spot that would allow me to sit without feeling like I was going to pass out. "Oooh, God, this hurts," I said softly to Karl, wincing as my voice caught in my throat. "Would you take a look and see if you can see anything back there, like a bruise or something?" I leaned over toward the edge of my side of the bed so Karl could lift the covers and take a look.

"Oh yeah," Karl confirmed grimly. "Your entire lower back and the top of your butt cheeks are completely purple." He looked at me seriously as his eyes met mine. "It's gross," he said, making a face.

"I hardly even noticed how much this hurt yesterday," I said, wondering at how this could have happened overnight. "It sure makes it hard to find a comfortable position!" I laughed, trying to make light of the situation. Karl was visibly upset, and even though we'd talked a lot last night, I could tell he was getting angry again at the breadth of my injuries.

"What'd you guys get from The Rabbit?" I asked Daniel and Max, pointedly shifting our attention from my bruises to the boys' baskets. Virtually oblivious to what was going on between their father and me, they joyfully dug through their piles of Easter grass and showed us their prizes.

Soon after, Karl and the boys got ready and left for church. There was no way I could make it to Mass today, Easter or not, and we agreed that it would be easier on all of us if I was free to hobble about our bedroom on my own, taking however long I required to get into the shower, and simply having some time to myself. I yearned to write in my journal. I needed to sort out what was going on between Karl and me and grope for a deeper understanding of the events of the last few days.

Settling into the unique super-quiet of a house that's just emptied itself of its children, I grabbed my journal from the pile of books beside my bed. I couldn't make one more move, or take a shower, until I poured my feelings and observations onto the lined paper of my spiral notebook.

"Karl and I are still not truly connecting," I began. *"We're quite discordant. He feels like I don't listen to him."* Boy, am I *lucky I didn't hurt my right hand,* I thought to myself. *I'd go nuts if I couldn't write in my journal.*

My heart hurt as I wrote out my worries about our relationship. Despite our talk last night, Karl had once again withdrawn from me as we'd looked through our Easter baskets and talked to the kids. I'd called him on it while watching him get dressed for church . . .

"What's wrong?" I'd asked, getting weary of feeling his energy flip up and down, his emotions toward me surging from passion and deep worry, then plummeting to something that felt like sneering disdain. Whatever it was that he was thinking, it was obviously making him upset. The trick was getting him to *say* what he was really thinking.

"Nothing." My stomach tightened at his clipped, predictable response. God, I was getting sick of having to drag every single thing out of him.

"Come on," I countered back at him. "Your whole attitude toward me changed as we were looking at our baskets. I felt it. Don't deny it." I was determined not to let him make me feel like I was making it up in my head. For a moment, he didn't answer and I thought he was going to continue ignoring my pleas for communication.

"You never listen to me," he hissed, whirling around from the mirror in which he'd been watching himself tying and re-tying his tie.

"What?" I asked in surprise. For the life of me, I didn't know where this was coming from.

"You never listen to me," he repeated, without additional explanation.

"What in the world are you talking about?"

"That buffalo thing you gave me for Easter," he snarled. "It's stupid; I hate it."

I flinched at his words. *Talk about looking a gift horse in the mouth, you shit head.* The 'buffalo thing' to which he was referring was a solid piece of ceramic material in the form and size of an egg, with the face and shoulders of a buffalo sculpted in raised relief on one side. I'd seen it a few weeks before and thought it would be a cute thing to put in Karl's basket since Catherine had encouraged him at our last gathering to meditate on the buffalo, suggesting it was one of his totems.

"So*rry*," I said, neither feeling nor sounding one whit sorry. "But what does that have to do with me supposedly not listening to you?"

"Nothing. Forget it." He turned his back on me again and began another attempt at tying his tie.

"Will you knock it off?" I raised my voice, trying to will him to turn back around and face me. "Talk to me. What do you mean I don't listen to you?"

"How many times have I told you that I don't think Buffalo is my totem?" he retorted angrily.

I paused before I answered him, recognizing that he was right. He had told me several times during our walks over the past couple of weeks that he thought Catherine was wrong about Buffalo being his totem. I'd listened to him and tried to embrace his belief, but I just couldn't get past the feeling that his vehement denial and protestations were too shrill somehow. There was something about Buffalo, some aspect to the qualities of this animal as a totem, that he was absolutely refusing to recognize within himself.

"You're right," I conceded. He looked at me with a mixture of surprise and lingering anger in his eyes. I took a deep breath. Did I want to take this any further? Part of me wanted to just shut up about it and act contrite. The other, more vocal part of myself, wanted to explain why I'd ignored his rejection of Buffalo and help him see how he was fooling himself.

For a few minutes, I chose silence. And that's where we sat, in silence, as he completed dressing and I helped Max get into his pin-striped pants, vest and jacket that I'd bought for the holiday. As a finishing touch, his red bow tie was a hit and he ran downstairs to show it off to his brother.

As Max clumped down the wooden stairs to the kitchen, I heard Karl mumble something under his breath, the first thing he'd said since our last little interchange.

"What did you say?" I asked. "Were you talking to me?"

"I said, I'm a Wolf, not a Buffalo."

"Oh," I replied, nodding my head as if it made sense to me. I tried to stifle a laugh, and luckily succeeded, because Karl was obviously seeing no humor in this situation; the look on his face was pained. "Why do you think having Wolf as a totem is any better than having Buffalo?"

"I *don't* think it's any better," he retorted icily.

"Oh, OK," I said agreeably, trying to sound like I believed him.

"I just know myself," he glared at me pointedly, his implication clear.

"Oh, that's right," I responded, sarcasm loaded and ready to fire. "This from the man who sneaks cigarettes and deliberately eats food that's bad for him, even though he's prone to heart disease, and then lies about it? Sure Karl, you know yourself," I sneered. "You refuse to look at yourself and take responsibility for what you're doing. You blame me for not listening to you and not being supportive and all the other stuff you find fault with me for, and then use it as an excuse to abuse yourself. But really it's you. You aren't listening to yourself. I'm sick of being blamed for causing you 'stress' and 'making' you smoke. At least if you're going to blame me for something, Karl, blame me for something that's even remotely possible. But don't blame me for not listening to you. I listen to you far more than you listen to yourself."

Karl said nothing. He sat on the edge of his side of our bed and seemed to be staring into his closet. I couldn't tell if I had gotten through to him and, at that moment, I didn't care. My heart was thumping in my chest and I couldn't remain in bed any longer, despite my previous desire to stay there until they had left for church. I hopped out of bed, gritting my teeth, willing myself not to groan or grimace, and began tugging at the sheets and blankets in an effort to make my side of the bed.

"And you *are* judging the Buffalo," I continued, not satisfied to let the matter drop. "I know you're resisting the lessons Buffalo has to teach you, and I'm completely at a loss as to why you're running away from it. But you are—I can see it, clear as day." Gently, I sat down beside him. "And I'd only be blowing smoke up your ass if I continued to pretend that I agree with you. You're not looking at yourself clearly, hon, and I'm not going to just sit by and be a yes-man to your distortions."

"No one could ever accuse you of being that," Karl said quietly. He paused, opened his mouth as if to say more, but closed it without saying another word.

"Well, I'm sorry you hated your buffalo so much," I said earnestly, and honestly. "But I'm not sorry I gave it to you. It still feels like it was the right thing to do."

Karl glanced at the red digital numbers of his clock radio perched atop the wooden table beside the bed. "We'd better get going or we won't get a seat," he commented.

As I related this in my journal and tried to articulate the feelings that coursed through me as we'd argued, I came to a startling conclusion:

"Maybe my lesson is to simply love him and allow him to follow his own path—even if he chooses one that I feel is not the 'right' one for him. Who am I to say which is right? With respect to his smoking (and then lying about it), there really is no need for me to involve myself emotionally in any of these issues. It really is his body and his choice. He knows the risks. Where I have to re-

lease the hook is my heart—where those passionate feelings reside that are stirred up when I consider that his choice to hurt himself either carelessly *ignores the impact it vicariously has on me and the boys or* deliberately *ignores the possible ramifications. That's where my hook is—I feel like he doesn't love me or the boys enough to quit these games he's playing with his health . . .*

From my perspective, it looks to me as though he is consciously and deliberately engaging in these activities in order to flirt with death. And it's not even that he's flirting with death so much (that bothers me as the fact that) he's screwing around doing that stuff when we could be focussing together on creating a life that we don't even dream is possible."

And as I began to recognize the need for detachment in observing Karl's behavior, I extended the same logic to myself. It was easy for me to see what Karl was doing to block his spiritual growth. It was also clear to me that only Karl could decide to see it for himself. My job was to uncover my own modes of sabotaging my spiritual growth and begin to address them—*right now.*

Despite my physical discomfort, I found the words pouring out of my pen and into my journal. A seed of understanding was taking root in the center of my being and starting to spread up, throughout my body and, finally, into my mind. I didn't 'figure it out' or in any other way intellectually piece the puzzle together. It simply came together before my eyes as I wrote:

"I know that this whole occurrence was a warning—most probably having to do with power and its misuse—or perhaps mainly in my case at this point, . . . a denial of the existence of power—or a flippant disregard for it. (. . .) I need to focus on letting go of the things I constantly repeat in my (own) subconscious efforts to block my spiritual growth.

Like this whole power and awareness issue. I must stop denying what I am capable of expressing. The message is clear: if I continue to deny or to be flip and irreverent about power, I will be killed by it. It is not meant to be toyed with, nor is it capable of being ignored once it has been discovered (or uncovered). It must be respected. But it also must be cultivated. (. . .) Although I do not know at this very moment where the Universe will (ask) me to utilize this power, I am OK with that. I understand that I will be shown when the time is right. Until then I must practice. I must remain open to ONLY the highest and very best guidance given me by the Creator.

(. . .) I have been far too preoccupied with the externals (in my life)—most especially my business—but I am ready to move on. To start flying! Karl is OK. I love him so very much. We have far to travel."

An inexplicable and completely unexpected joy filled my heart. As if acknowledging my discovery, sunshine splashed across the covers of my bed, gilding everything in my room with a golden light. Closing my spiral notebook, I gathered my favorite bath towel, hung it over the front of the walker we'd borrowed from my parents, and made my way ever so gingerly to the bathroom.

I *felt* the message contained in my fall. I knew the power of which I'd just written. It was up to me to claim my gift and stop denying its existence.

I have owl medicine, I thought to myself, as I slipped into the comforting embrace of a hot bath. Little did I know how soon I would be called upon to use and trust my 'gift.'

Owl

Deception

*O*wl medicine is symbolically associated with clairvoyance, astral projection, and magic, both black and white. Owl is called Night Eagle on several medicine wheels used by Amerindian teachers. Traditionally, Owl sits in the East, the place of illumination. Since time immemorial, humanity has been afraid of the night, the dark, and the unseen — waiting fearfully for the first crack of morning light. Conversely, night is Owl's friend.

Owl hunts its prey at night. Not only can Owl see in the dark, it can also accurately pinpoint and identify any sound. This gives it a great advantage when seeking food. Owls are the night hunters. Some Native people are fearful of Owl and call its feathers "deceiver feathers." An Owl feather is silent. You cannot hear Owl when it flies, but its prey definitely knows when it strikes, for its beak and talons are razor sharp.

Owl is oftentimes the medicine of sorcerers and witches. If Owl is your medicine, you will be drawn to magical practices and perhaps explore the dark arts. You should resist any temptation to practice black magic or any art that takes energy away from another person or being. If you have Owl medicine, these night birds *will have a tendency to collect around you, even in the daytime, because they recognize a kinship with you.*

Is it any wonder that in many cultures Owl is a symbol for wisdom? This is because Owl can see that which others cannot, which is the essence of true wisdom. Where others are deceived, Owl sees and knows what is there.

Athena, the Greek goddess of wisdom, had a companion Owl on her shoulder which revealed unseen truths to her. Owl had the ability to light up Athena's blind side, enabling her to speak the whole truth, as opposed to only a half truth.

If Owl is your personal medicine, no one can deceive you about what they are doing, no matter how they try to disguise or hide it from you. You may be a little frightening to be around, since so many people have ulterior motives which you see right through. If you are unaware of your medicine power, you may take your keen insights and abilities for granted. Others never do. You may frighten them and reflect their blindness, for you cannot be fooled. Owl medicine people know more about an individual's inner life than that person knows about herself or himself.

If you have pulled the Owl card, you are being asked to use your powers of keen, silent observation to intuit some life situation. Owl is befriending you and aiding you in seeing the total truth. Owl can bring you messages in the night through dreams or meditation. Pay attention to the signals and omens. The truth always brings further enlightenment.

-from *Medicine Cards*
by Jamie Sams and David Carson

CHAPTER THIRTY THREE

I already knew I was onto something. The sun 'happening' to break out from behind the clouds that had shrouded our area for several days, at the very moment I put it all together, was just another synchronistic confirmation. But when I started reading *Shouting at the Wolf* while taking a hot bath in Dead Sea salts, leaning back on the pink bath pillow the Easter Bunny had brought me in my basket, prickles rose like waves on my scalp. The words of the author were uncannily timely to my understanding and appreciation of my not-so-accidental brush with death.

I read the book voraciously, stopping only occasionally to wonder aloud at the astonishing manner, and timing, of my finding and purchasing it. The insights I'd just made as I wrote in my journal were not by any stretch of the imagination 'ordinary,' and I knew that there were precious few people with whom I could explore them further. Yet here I was, holding a book that spoke to me as if I'd just related my story to the author herself. Here I was, reading a book that point-blank confirmed that my feelings and insights were right on.

Karl was surprised when he and the boys arrived home from church and found me dressed and sitting on the edge of the bed. "Wow, what came over you?" he asked, as he tiptoed up the first three steps from the kitchen to peek into the bedroom. "I thought you might have fallen back asleep after we left."

"No, I didn't go back to bed. I wrote in my journal and took a bath." I could feel satisfaction radiating from my face. There was so much to tell Karl, but I wasn't sure where to begin.

"That's great!"

"I had a couple of 'ahas' while I was writing, " I began, testing the waters to see if he was interested in talking. "I think I'm getting an idea as to what was really going on when I fell."

"Really? I want to hear all about it." He glanced behind himself, down the spiral stairway to the kitchen. "Can you make it down the stairs by yourself or do you want some help?"

"No, that's OK. I can do it myself," I replied, waving my hand to ward off his assistance.

"I thought I'd make some Bisquick pancakes for Easter breakfast," he said brightly. "What do you think?"

"Pancakes! Yeah!" Daniel yelled. He was at the foot of our bed rifling through his Easter basket, practically inhaling his jellybeans.

"Pancakes, yeah! Pancakes, yeah!" echoed Max.

"Hey!" I said to Daniel. "Enough of the candy already. Wait until after we've had breakfast." I turned to his father and rolled my eyes. "Pancakes sound like a great idea," I responded, appreciating his offer. "You sure you don't mind?"

"No, not at all. And then you can tell me what you've discovered," he added with an encouraging smile. His interest felt genuine and his manner was easy and open. I was shocked at the difference in his attitude. Was it just the change in my outlook or had he changed too?

As if hearing my silent question, Karl added, "I did some thinking at church about what you said this morning—and I can see your point."

"Really?" I responded, surprised that he'd come around so quickly.

"Yeah, I've been feeling pretty awful lately," he admitted, climbing a couple more stairs and sitting on the bedroom floor, at the threshold, leaning his back against the doorjamb. "And I have been blaming you for it."

I waited, curious to see where this was going.

He picked a piece of lint off his pants and rolled it between his fingers. "I figure maybe I should try meditating on Buffalo to see if anything comes to me. I'll read the story in the Medicine Cards, too. Maybe that will help." He looked up at me and I was surprised by the sadness in his eyes.

"That's a good idea," I encouraged him. "There must be something there, don't you think? Something you need to look at and learn about yourself?" I paused, thinking about his declaration earlier in the day. "Why else would you be fighting it so hard?" I laughed. "It is funny when you think about it from a distance."

"What do you mean?"

"Just that you got so annoyed at being told that a particular animal is here to guide you. I think it's funny that you would judge one animal to be better than another—as if it's a beauty contest or something."

"Yeah, I guess," he said reluctantly, a smile turning up the corners of his mouth. He stood up and stretched, his hands gripping the top of the doorway, and then turned to go down to the kitchen.

"Hey," I said, not wanting to break our connection. He turned toward me yet remained silent. The smile still played on his face, but sadness lingered in his eyes.

Easter afternoon turned out to be the complete antithesis of Good Friday. Bright sunshine spilled from the sky, warming the air enough to invite gardening and yard work. After breakfast, the boys gathered their trucks and M.U.S.C.L.E. men and set up camp at the edge of the lawn, in a small muddy dirt pile, just off the edge of the porch. Karl began working his flowerbeds, planting some bulbs that had long been laying around in the cellar stairway. I had no choice but to sit on the porch and soak up the sunshine, while continuing to devour my book.

Over breakfast I had read to Karl what I'd written in my journal. I described the feelings and insights that had poured from my pen and how the sunshine had penetrated the clouds at the height of my breakthrough. Then I read him a snippet from *Shouting at the Wolf*:

> "' . . . We don't hear the words of the wind anymore, or the messages of the birds. We neither hear nor see the all-life because we have turned away from it and, in a very real way, also turned away from ourselves, because the force that animates and forms stones and water is the same force that animates and forms human beings. In losing touch with the life surrounding us, we have lost contact with the God-in-all and, therefore, with ourselves.'"

"Holy cow," commented Karl. "you couldn't have asked for more obvious or immediate confirmation."

"I know! She specifically refers to stones and water—the two elements I encountered most . . . *forcefully* the other day. And she so accurately describes the disconnection I felt, too—with myself, God, the Universe . . . ."

"It almost makes my heart ache."

"Yes. The anger and despair I screamed at the elements were the essence of a heart and soul ache. But wait—there's more." I turned the pages of the book eagerly, finding the spot I wanted to read to him next. "Do you remember what I burned in our fire walk? What I sacrificed in order to move forward on my path?"

Karl frowned.

"Do you even remember what *you* sacrificed?" I asked with a laugh, suddenly sure he didn't.

He ignored me. "Umm, was it guilt?" he guessed.

"No, fear," I prodded. "I made a conscious effort to let go of my constant fear of failing everybody and everything. Remember?"

"Oh yeah, that's right," Karl said, leaning back in his chair.

"Well get this," I said opening the book again. "She's talking about the 'good news' and the 'bad news' associated with following a path aligned with Spirit. The way she describes the good news is pretty much how we've been experiencing life lately. You know, that feeling of being connected to everything? The feeling that we're here for a reason and that there are no such things as coincidences?" I searched for more examples of how much our lives had changed since we began our studies in earnest. "She even describes that energized feeling we get when we discuss and live what we're learning."

Karl nodded his head, prompting me to cut to the chase. "Yeah? What's the bad news?"

"Listen:

> 'The bad news is that once you've asserted yourself in the presence of Spirit, brought yourself out into the Light, you are going to be, at some time and in some way, attacked by spirits of darkness. It is inevitable. For every human being who enlivens the world by mating his consciousness with Spirit, there is a little less fear in the world. And fear is what keeps beings of the darkness alive and functioning.'"

I closed the book on my finger again and looked up at Karl. "What do you make of that?"

"I don't know," Karl hesitated. I waited while he digested the words. Would he make the same connection I had? "Do you think we're attracting the attention of darkness by living our lives more aware of the Light?"

"Yeah, that's kind of what I was thinking . . . ."

"And this fear stuff," he continued. "Now I'm seeing it! Ever since you sacrificed the fear in your life, it's as if situations keep coming up in which you're forced to face it, and feel it, again and again. It's as if you—or we—are being challenged by the darkness."

I nodded, glad that he saw it too, but not at all thrilled with the reality it suggested.

Taking a break from my reading, I turned the book upside down on my lap, keeping my place by having the pages straddle my leg. Closing my eyes, I rested my head on the back of the plastic-latticed lounge chair, absorbing the warmth of the spring sunshine. I was suddenly acutely aware of the cacophony of life surrounding me. Max and Daniel, both sprawled on the ground in front of me, were making airplane and siren noises, crashing cars into one another, and giving voices to their 'guys.' I could hear blue jays raucously marking their territories, redheaded woodpeckers issuing their whistle-like call between bouts of furious pecking, and the sweet serenade of the fifteen robins I'd counted a few minutes before, playing tag in the yard. Sparrows chattered incessantly. Overnight, Spring had arrived with a flourish.

I took a deep breath of sweet, warm air. Surrounded by all of this goodness, it was almost unbelievable to find myself reading about the forces of darkness and how negative energy feeds on anger, fear, hate, and self-loathing. But honestly, I thought to myself, it doesn't come as much of a surprise. Those emotions are powerful and inherently destructive, so the fact that they would feed darkness and darkness would feed them isn't that big of a revelation. The true surprise, for me, was realizing how *denial* of the existence of evil is its greatest source of power. I didn't want to see the 'dark side,' it was true. I could feel my mind frantically trying to deny the credibility of what I was reading. I desperately wanted to believe that if I didn't think about evil, if I didn't give it power by believing in it, I could escape having to deal with it at all.

But the juxtaposition of this glorious day with the violent, stormy one of only two days before, and the reflection of those opposites in my thoughts and feelings on those days, reminded me that I could no longer afford to be naive. The more I read, the clearer it became that darkness was gaining a foothold in our world each and every time we turned our head away from its existence in our daily lives.

Unless they have studied metaphysics, most people don't believe that thoughts, in and of themselves, have any influence on the world. Actions, we are told from a very young age, speak louder than words. Implicit in this adage is the belief that words speak louder than thoughts. Consequently, many of us mistakenly assume that thoughts have no real power *unless we act on them*.

But as I'd learned through the readings assigned by Catherine, as well as through her lectures and other books I'd read on my own, thoughts are energy, even if we cannot see them. Words and actions are simply more forceful directions of the energies of our thoughts. By refusing to believe that evil exists, and simultaneously refusing to take responsibility for our thoughts, we inadvertently leave the door ajar for darkness to slip in, unnoticed because it is disbelieved.

I could feel myself trying to discount the responsibility that following this line of thought would place on me. Surely it's not possible to be happy all the time?! Of course it's not, I answered myself, suddenly aware of my internal dialogue. But how often have I wallowed in my negativity lately? Feeling sad or angry or confused in response to events that occur in day to day life is almost inevitable. But *staying* with those feelings, indulging in constant mental repetition of how a situation is 'unfair' or obsessing over the way a person has 'wronged' us, gives energy to them. They grow and seem to demand more and more of our attention. Soon we find that we have less energy available to us for our other thoughts and activities.

As I sat on my porch thinking this through, I could see how remaining in a negative frame of mind is a choice, a choice that we're all forced to make many times every day. I could see how simple carelessness or lack of awareness could, if unchecked, lead to a veritable feast for evil, if indeed it finds nourishment in negativity. For most people, taking a stand against the darkness and malignance we see in the world begins and ends with actively taking responsibility for our own thoughts, words, and deeds. It is in the little things, allowing those small, seemingly unimportant indulgences of dark thoughts to occur over and over, that darkness is most able to wallow and grow fat.

Of course evil doesn't care whether we believe in it! It relishes our disbelief, because when people don't believe, they are far more cavalier and irresponsible with their thoughts, speech, and actions. What do they need to be careful of? From what do they need to protect themselves if evil does not exist?

Knowing the power of my thoughts, I have a responsibility to myself, my family, and my world to watch them carefully. Each time I choose to let go of my anger, to knock off my self-pity, to forego saying something mean about my neighbor, I retain and reinforce my integrity, thereby enhancing my life force and reducing the food supply for evil.

I could see the wisdom of looking at the world this way. It made sense to me on a gut level. I had learned, early on in my studies, of the power of *thought*. Yet I'd never before considered how ignoring the existence of evil actually enhanced its ability to flourish. With an almost audible 'click' the connection was made. I knew I could no longer continue shirking my responsibility.

Returning my attention to my book, I began to read the author's account of how she was forced to recognize the existence of evil in the world. My eyes flitted across the pages, absorbed in her tale. The more I read, however, the more I felt a growing sense of horror and reluctant corroboration of suspicions I'd only barely allowed myself to entertain.

"Oh Karl," I groaned, finally incapable of maintaining my silence. "I can't believe what I'm reading," I said, fear creeping into my voice despite my best effort to keep it out.

Karl looked up from his digging, sweat dripping down the sides of his face and off the tip of his nose. "What is it?"

"This book," I said, gesturing with the paperback I held in my right hand. "It's flipping me out."

"Why? What's wrong? I thought you liked that book," he said as he sat down on the edge of the porch, his feet resting on the concrete steps. Before I could begin, he added,"Hang on a second; let me get an iced tea. You need yours refreshed?"

"No thanks," I replied. "I'm sorry I can't get up and get you something myself. It looks really beautiful over there," I added, gesturing with my chin toward the flower bed bordering our driveway.

"Thanks!" he said brightly, as the screen door banged shut behind him. Not a minute later, he returned, iced tea in hand. "Alright," he said, settling comfortably into the cushions of the glider beside me. "What's the matter?"

"This book is hitting me way too close for comfort," I began, wishing I didn't have to actually talk about it. I was filled with conflicting emotions, and I didn't want Karl to think I'd gone over the edge.

"How?"

"Well, I'm reading this woman's account of how she was forced to confront and ultimately do battle with evil," I began again. "Like us, she didn't want to believe that evil exists either. Kind of, you know, if you don't think about it and give it power, it won't have anything to do with you?" I said, gesturing with my hands, almost as if I were trying to pull the words out of myself.

"Yeah," Karl encouraged.

"Well, the similarities between her experiences and the strange way Beth's been acting towards me is making me think that I may be under psychic attack." I winced. There, I'd said it. I barely gave him a chance to respond. "Do you think I'm nuts?" I asked anxiously.

"No, I don't," he replied matter-of-factly.

"Why don't you think I'm crazy?" I asked, wondering at his

easy acceptance of my statement and suspecting he might be patronizing me. There was a part of me that thought I might be imagining this or at least blowing it out of proportion. This was not the first time I'd heard of psychic attacks. In fact, I'd read about them in various texts as I pursued my studies. But I honestly never gave their existence much attention or credence. I certainly never thought they would have any bearing on my own life! And here was Karl, calmly accepting my announcement that I suspected I—and probably we—were under attack.

"Think about it for a minute," he said in a logical tone of voice. "With what we know about energy and everything, doesn't it make sense that, if we can be attacked physically, we can be attacked psychically as well? We know invisible forces exist. Why would it be such a great leap to accept that the invisible power of an individual could be directed and used to try to harm another?" He looked at me with such a serious, matter-of-fact look on his face that I was momentarily rendered speechless. "We can't see electricity, for heaven's sake, and that's real!" he added in exasperation. "And that can be used to either light up our houses in the dark or electrocute someone. It's all a matter of intent."

I just stared at him and smiled. Shaking my head in disbelief, I commented, "You never cease to amaze me."

Karl grinned. "Yeah, well, that's just to keep you interested," he teased. But his eyebrows quickly knit together again in an expression of concern. "Seriously though, Lis," he added. "I don't think you're crazy for thinking you might be under attack. But I do want to know why you think so."

"You know how strange Beth has been acting since we got home from New Mexico," I began, "particularly toward me. Don't you?" Karl nodded. "The talking behind my back to both Ellen and Catherine, telling Ellen that I was the one who was acting strange since we came back, and all that?" I added, trying to refresh his recollection with specifics.

"Yup," he said. "And how she even told Ellen that Catherine warned her that you were the owl?" he added. "*That* was weird."

"Right, right," I said, nodding my head. "And now she's become this acolyte to Catherine, putting all these strange religious overtones on our studies," I continued.

"But why does that make you think you're under psychic attack? And do you think you're being attacked by Beth?"

"Not necessarily," I said, shaking my head. "There's no telling who—or even what, for that matter—is actually behind the attack." I hesitated. I didn't even want to entertain the possibility, but I had to say it. "For all we know, it could be Catherine. Or something dark that's using them both," I said, shrugging my shoulders uncomfortably. "And you're right," I continued. "None of this by itself would make me think I'm under attack. But think about this. Beth was warned by Catherine to be wary of 'my owl,' which I am just starting to accept is my ability to tell when somebody's bullshitting me—or themselves."

"And why would she warn her if she—or they—had nothing to hide?" Karl asked, following my train of thought.

"Exactly! But if that's true, just for the sake of argument, then what are they so afraid I'm going to see?" I asked, honestly puzzled. "There's that business over the money they collected at the seminar," I mused. "But I can't imagine that they'd attack me over that . . . and for all I know, Beth has given the money to the shelter by now."

"That's true."

"I'll tell you what really spooked me," I said. "Did I tell you Beth called me at the office on Friday?"

"No!" said Karl, sounding surprised. "What did she have to say? You haven't talked to her in weeks, have you?"

"No, I haven't. In fact, I hadn't heard from her in weeks—since that last meeting we had at her house the day after Catherine gave the seminar."

"What did she have to say?"

"It was very strange," I said, remembering how odd Beth had sounded on the telephone. "The whole conversation was incredibly superficial, as if there was some other reason that she was calling but she wasn't admitting it."

"What did you guys talk about?"

"Nothing, really. She told me how she'd been at some convention or something the weekend before," I began. "I guess it must have been last weekend," I said, more to myself than to Karl. "Hm! With Catherine, now that I think about it!" I looked at Karl in surprise. "That seems weird, doesn't it? How all of a sudden Catherine is spending so much time with only one of her students?" I shook my head. I did not want to scrutinize this situation any further.

"Why do you think she told you that she'd spent the weekend with Catherine? To make you jealous?"

"Maybe," I agreed. "But why?" I threw up my hand in bewilderment. "Why would I care if she and Catherine are becoming friends? I remember thinking to myself when she said it that it seemed uncharacteristic of Catherine, but then it seemed to just blip out of my mind. Until just now," I added. I stared at the boys, still playing in the dirt, their jackets flung toward the steps of the porch. What else had we talked about? It was only two days ago, but it seemed like months had gone by.

"I remember she talked on and on about 'the church' and how excited she was about the prospect of ordination."

Karl groaned and his shoulders sagged.

"I know," I said, nodding in agreement. "My feelings exactly. But anyway, I remember thinking how strange it was that she never talked about our association with Catherine as a school anymore. It's always, 'the church this, the church that.' And even more creepy," I added, the conversation starting to come back to me more clearly as I spoke, "was this feeling I had that nothing she was saying to me was wholly truthful. I don't know why . . . I mean, I don't know why she would have any reason to deliberately call me up to tell me things that weren't true. You know?" I asked, feeling perplexed. "But there was this tinny ring to her voice that made me extremely uncomfortable." I shivered and grimaced in distaste as I recalled the bizarre flavor of our conversation.

"That is peculiar," agreed Karl.

"There's more, though," I said mysteriously. "And this is the part that flipped me out when I was reading my book," I said, again wrinkling my nose. "Not long after I hung up with Beth I received a delivery at the office."

"A delivery?" asked Karl. "Of what?"

"Flowers. I thought they were from you."

"I didn't send you flowers," Karl said, his voice an odd mixture of indignation and sheepishness.

"I *know* that," I replied, exasperation tingeing my voice. "They were from Beth."

"Get out of here," Karl responded, his eyes widening. "Maybe that's why she called then? To see if you got them?" he suggested, his voice sounding hopeful. Neither of us wanted to think ill of our friend.

"I tried to tell myself that too," I admitted. "But as much as I wanted to believe it, I just couldn't make it stick."

"So what's so weird about that, though, in the grand scheme of things?" Karl asked.

"I was reading about this author's personal experience of confronting evil," I said, gesturing again to the book in my lap, "and seeing way too many parallels for my taste, I might add—when I came to this part." I picked up the book and began to read aloud.

> "'. . . (C)ut flowers can be programmed, or magnetized, with either positive or negative energy. (. . .) Picked flowers, still alive but quickly losing their life force, are vulnerable. Once severed from their roots, they are separated from the spirit force that oversees plant life. Still, they are not dead, and their energy can be appropriated for good or evil, as can the energy of human beings.'"

I closed the book and looked at Karl for a reaction.

"Oh man," he said, shifting uneasily in the glider. "Do you really believe that? Do you think that's possible?"

"Well, when I first read this, I did find it a bit incredible," I admitted. "I mean, think of all the millions of bouquets and arrangments that are bought or sent every single day. Wouldn't it lead to incredible paranoia to think that all those cut flowers are 'programmed?' But then I realized that most people *do* send flowers with a specific intent behind them, usually an expression of love or sympathy. When I looked at how popular and effective flower-giving is as a means of showing people we care, in conjunction with this new perspective regarding *energy*, the premise didn't seem as far-fetched as it had originally."

"I see what you mean!" Karl exclaimed. "Yeah, it almost makes the effectiveness of the whole 'flower sending' custom make even more sense. On one level, people are influenced by the beauty, colors, and sweet scents of the flowers themselves. But on another level, they're receiving the love or concern or apology or whatever *intent* is sent with the flowers." He looked at me pointedly and added, "Which is usually something positive!"

"Yup. But just because that is what's *usually* done doesn't mean it is what's always done. A person knowledgable about energy and life force could certainly manipulate it otherwise, just as easily."

"So what are you saying, Lis?"

I looked at Karl, my heart pounding uncomfortably at the base of my throat.

"Well, I'm not saying I fell *because* of those flowers. I was indulging in self-pity way before they even arrived. But I can see that, within a few hours of receiving my 'gift,' I'd left the office in an even fouler mood than I'd arrived, made my way to the book-store where this book practically jumped off the shelf at me, and then found myself performing a swan dive into the rocks at the base of the creek. I can tell you that my negative feelings that afternoon were amplified way beyond anything I've ever felt before. I was spewing rage, helplessness, and disbelief—and I can tell you that darkness nearly stole my life."

CHAPTER THIRTY FOUR

"I'm going to put my hands back in the dirt," Karl said abruptly, as he stood up to return to his gardening. "I need to give this time to settle."

"You seem upset. Is it because you *are* starting to think I'm nuts or is it because of what we're possibly . . . discovering?" I asked, regretting the edge of paranoia in my voice. *I want some reassurance here Karl. Please don't just get up and run away.*

"Well?" he said, laughing humorlessly and turning his hands up in a puzzled gesture. "I am upset. You almost died the other day." He stared off the porch, away from me, obviously somewhere else in his mind. Breaking his reverie after a few moments, he turned again toward me, his eyes tender. "I love you, Lisa, and I don't think you're nuts."

"Thanks, Karl," I said. "I love you too." I smiled and reached for his hand. "I don't think I could stand it if I had to face this without you."

"You won't," he reassured me, squeezing my hand three times, our unspoken *I love you.* "Problem is, I feel as enraged at the thought that you were psychically attacked as I would if you'd been physically attacked. I can feel it, right in here," he said, tapping his chest with his free hand.

He was right; it was a problem. I could see the rage rippling just under the surface of his emotions, glittering in his blue eyes and giving them an uncharacteristically steely tint.

"Don't give in to the rage," I said, issuing a caution I was only beginning to grasp myself. "That will only give whatever or whoever is attacking us more power."

Karl looked at me, displeasure flickering across his face. "I know you're probably right," he began, "but —"

"But nothing," I interrupted, not wanting him to finish his thought. "We've got to keep ourselves in balance! We're being shown this for a reason!" I paused, wondering what in the world that reason could be. Karl looked at me, obviously wondering the same thing. "We're being shown it so we can deal with it. Now that we're seeing that evil exists and isn't just a figment of fairy tales and bible stories, we have to learn how to protect ourselves." I looked at him and then, pointedly, looked at my battered body.

"How?" Karl asked. "How do we do that?"

"First of all, we have to keep our thoughts clear and positive. We can't give in to anger, fear, or desire for revenge, because they're all negative thought forms which will only serve to weaken us and strengthen them—or it—or *whatever*."

"OK," Karl agreed. "But there must be more that we can do?"

"I'm sure there is," I responded, letting go of Karl's hand and picking up the book again. "But I haven't gotten there yet."

"Oh!" Karl said, smiling again. "Then get crackin' woman!" he kidded. "While you do that, I'm going to put my hands back in the earth again. *That* seems to work for me!" He stood at the edge of the porch and faced the afternoon sun, his eyes closed. Clasping his hands together, he raised his arms above his head in a long, languid stretch.

"What a day," groaned Karl, as he eased himself into bed, gathering the covers around himself. It was only 9:30 p.m., but the boys were already asleep and Karl and I were up in our room. "I can't believe how sore I am, just from one day's work in the garden!"

I grunted in sympathy, my foot resting atop three pillows. As the day had worn on the swelling had increased. "But it did end up being a great day, didn't it?" I asked. "Everything seemed so much brighter and lighter. It truly felt like *Easter*."

"I have to admit it. I feel better tonight than I have in a long time. Even considering what you've learned," he said, gesturing with his chin toward the book that lay on the covers between us.

"I wish I'd had a chance to get more read," I said apologetically. "After our conversation, I just seemed to run out of steam."

"Yeah," Karl laughed. "Nothing like taking a little nappy in the sun, huh?"

"Shut up," I snapped, feigning anger. "But guess what?" I asked, a twinkle in my eyes.

"What?"

"When I was sitting in the bathroom while Max was taking his bath, I picked a rune on the rest of the day," I said. "Guess what I picked?"

"Not Hagalaz again, I hope." Over dinner I'd told Karl more about my morning at the office on Friday, including choosing the rune of cataclysmic disruption.

"Nope," I laughed. "I chose Dagaz. *Breakthrough*."

CHAPTER THIRTY FIVE

I made myself go to the office the next day, even though I was too injured to drive on my own. I did some paperwork and made a few telephone calls, but the pain was tough to ignore. Worse than the physical discomfort, though, was the gnawing feeling in the pit of my stomach that my Easter weekend had uncovered a reality that commanded my attention—and demanded appropriate action. I was starting to regret the knowledge I was gaining.

While the boys were eating breakfast earlier, Karl and I had resumed our discussion about the possibility that dark influences may have played a factor in my fall.

"That's pretty cool that you picked Breakthrough last night," Karl said as he lifted his mug of coffee to his lips. He looked at the steam rising from the freshly ground brew and took a deep whiff. "I know we've read it a million times before, but I forget exactly what it means." He took a sip. "Aside from the obvious," he added. "Let's read it again."

"Sure," I said, reaching for the rune book which was buried under the morning newspaper. "The actual wording of the interpretation did send chills up my spine when I read it last night," I admitted, "even though I know it's a sign that we're on the right track." I looked in the table of contents and thumbed through the pages until I reached Dagaz. "Wait until you hear this:

DAGAZ. Breakthrough. Transformation Day. Here is the final Rune belonging to the Cycle of Initiation. Drawing Dagaz marks a major shift or breakthrough in the process of self-change, a complete transformation in attitude—a 180 degree turn. For some, the transition is so radical that they no longer continue to live the ordinary life in the ordinary way.

Because the timing is right, the outcome is assured although not, from the present vantage point, predictable. In each life there comes at least one moment which, if recognized and seized, transforms the course of that life forever. Rely, therefore, on radical trust, even though the moment may call for you to leap, empty-handed into the void. With this Rune your Warrior Nature reveals itself.

If Dagaz is followed by the Blank Rune, the magnitude of the transformation might be so total as to portend a death, the successful conclusion to your passage.

A major period of achievement and prosperity is often introduced by this Rune. The darkness is behind you; daylight has come. However, as always, you are reminded not to collapse yourself into the future or to behave recklessly in your new situation. A lot of hard work can be involved in a time of transformation. Undertake to do it joyfully."

I closed the book and reached for my coffee, giving Karl a chance to digest what I'd just read.

"Your *Warrior Nature* reveals itself?" he repeated in disbelief, emphasizing the words that had been following us around for six months. "Leaping empty-handed into the void?" His left eyebrow arched dramatically. "You kind of did that on Friday, didn't you?" he asked, facetiously trying to lighten things up.

"There's a lot of coincidence in this, isn't there?" I asked, feeling again the rustling of fear way down deep inside. "It sounds like we're just entering into the thick of things, doesn't it?"

Karl shook his head. "This is too weird," he declared.

"I want to agree with you," I said. "In fact, I do agree with you. This is way too bizarre for my taste, too. But do you think we can ignore all that's happened and all that we've been shown in the past couple of days? Do you think we can just go about our lives as if nothing has changed?"

A scowl crossed over Karl's face. "Well what are we supposed to do, Lis?" he asked, pushing his chair away from the table, the chair's wooden legs screeching their resistance. "I understand that we have to protect ourselves—which reminds me . . . ." He stood suddenly and walked into the living room, unlatched the small cubby in the bookcase and withdrew a smudge stick that we'd purchased in New Mexico. Returning to the kitchen, he lit the bundle of sage and sweetgrass with a wooden match.

"Spirits of the North, East, South, and West. Grandfather Sky and Mother Earth," he began, addressing each of the six sacred directions in a prayer of purification and protection. Bluish smoke billowed from the smudge stick, filling the kitchen with the sweet, comforting aroma of the native herbs.

Yes, I said to myself, *this is what we need.* I could feel my body relax, my shoulders easing ever so slightly from the rigid position I'd unconsciously been holding them in. I noticed Karl was looking at me expectantly. "Do you want me to help?" I asked, when I realized that he seemed at a loss for words.

"You're the one who's reading about protection," he mumbled, seeming embarrassed. "Isn't there something special we should say when we pray for protection?"

"I think the most important thing is our intention," I said, standing up and grabbing onto the edge of the table to steady myself. "You're doing great!"

Karl looked at me doubtfully.

"We want to be cleansed, purified, and protected," I suggested, trying to clarify for both of us exactly what our intentions were. "And we need to specifically tell the guardians of the cardinal directions that we may be under psychic attack and ask that they not allow their energies to be used against us."

Karl gave me a penetrating glance, his cocked eyebrow hinting at his internal battle with skepticism and his surprise at the precision of my words.

"I know, I know," I laughed nervously, shaking my head. "I woke up this morning and felt like I should look at *Shouting at the Wolf* again. I could feel myself resisting, but I picked it up and opened it anyway, just choosing a page at random. The first sentence I laid my eyes on gave specific instructions on how to pray for protection."

"Really?"

"Really. And the sentence wasn't at the beginning of a chapter or subchapter, either. It was just there, toward the top of the page, jumping out at me." I hesitated, watching the smoke curl toward Karl's head as he held the smudge stick with his right hand and kept his left hand cupped underneath to catch the ashes. "Then I paged back to find out the name of the subchapter I'd opened up to—just out of curiosity. It was 'Determining the Presence of Psychic Attack.'"

"Oh shit," Karl said, succinctly echoing my own sentiments exactly.

The office phone rang, jarring me from my recollection of our morning cleansing ceremony. I was grateful that we'd had a chance to smudge the boys and ourselves before Karl went to school and Max went to his babysitter. But I felt almost queasy now when I realized how close I'd come to simply forgetting that we needed to smudge. How could I be in the midst of this 'discovery' and then so easily forget to protect myself and my family?

I jumped when Sharon, my secretary, buzzed me on the intercom. Normally, I would leave my door open and she would just peek around the corner without getting up from her desk to tell me who was waiting on hold. But my door was closed today. I didn't want her to see me wincing in pain whenever I moved. And I didn't want her judging me if I happened to stare out the window as I contemplated all that was going on in my life.

My response to her page was a laugh, and she reacted in kind. "It's Ellen," Sharon advised with a chuckle. "Are you OK in there?"

"I'm fine," I assured her. "You just surprised me, that's all."

"All right, " she said. "Just checking."

I picked up the phone and pressed the line that was blinking. "Finally! Hi! Where have you been?" I nearly shouted into the receiver. I'd spoken to Ellen only very briefly on Saturday morning to tell her that I'd fallen. Even on Saturday morning, although I hadn't yet read any of *Shouting at the Wolf*, I'd had the feeling that somehow my awful attitude had contributed to my accident. For some odd reason, I'd felt compelled to suggest to Ellen that she be careful herself, keep her energy focussed on the positive. But I hadn't heard a word from her since. I couldn't believe she hadn't called to see how I was doing. She'd even forgotten completely that Friday was my birthday. Truth be told, by this morning, I'd begun struggling to suppress my hurt feelings.

"Hi," croaked a voice that sounded about a hundred years old. Instantly I felt a strong, seemingly irrational desire to hang up the phone. But I fought it.

"Ellen? What's going on? What's the matter?"

"I'm sick," came her reply. "Really out of it." I struggled with conflicting emotions. I could feel myself starting to be annoyed at her; I was irritated with the fact that she was now sick and seeking attention from me instead of acknowledging *my* injuries, *my* brush with death. Not once had she called to see how I was. In fact, she was only calling me now, I was sure, because I'd left two messages on her answering machine today, the second one simply asking her to let me know she was alive and all right. The more I'd read, both yesterday and today, and the more convinced I'd become that something foul was afoot, the more relieved I was that I'd had the instinctive presence of mind to warn Ellen to protect herself. Indeed, when I wasn't feeling sorry for myself, I'd begun to get worried about her lack of communication, which was why I'd left the last message on her machine.

"When did you get sick?" I asked, editing the swirl of thought that had just raced through my head.

"Sunday morning," she croaked again. "I just got worse and worse all day Sunday, then this morning I felt totally immobilized and helpless. I thought I was going to die," she said, breaking into a coughing spasm.

"You need to smudge," I said deliberately. "Did you do anything to protect yourself after we talked on Saturday?"

"No," she admitted. "But I was busy getting ready for Easter Sunday," she said a little defensively. "I was having my family over for dinner and I didn't have time to meditate or anything." She started coughing again, a deep, barking cough that sounded like it hurt. "I ended up spending the day in bed anyway," she grumbled.

"You need to smudge," I repeated, surprised that she hadn't yet asked how I was feeling but trying not to get invested in her lapse.

"You said that before," she replied, sounding vague and foggy, as if on death's doorstep. "That's that stuff you burn that you bought out in New Mexico, isn't it?"

"Yeah, but you can buy it around here," I responded. "It's used to cleanse and purify a person, place, or thing of negative energy. Native americans have used herbs—sage, and sometimes sweetgrass or cedar—for this purpose for thousands of years. You need to do it," I persisted. "Do you have a smudge stick of your own?"

"No . . . ."

"You really should get yourself one and smudge yourself, your family, and your house."

"I'm too sick," she stated unequivocally. Coughing punctuated her declaration.

"Look Ellen," I began, not wanting to launch into a full discussion, over the telephone, of what I'd been reading, but wishing
she would listen to me. "I don't think this is something to be
fooled with. I would bring a smudge stick over to your house
myself, but I don't have my car. *I can't drive*," I added, my first
reference to my own injuries.

"Why can't you drive?" she demanded. But before I could
answer she caught herself, and with a self-conscious laugh exclaimed, "Ooh! That's right! How are you?"

"I'm all right," I said, hurt and annoyed. Suddenly, I felt
totally exhausted and just wanted to hang up. I didn't want to get
angry, but I was finding it very difficult to remain detached. Not
only did I need to be detached over whether or not she cared
about me as a friend; I also needed to be detached over whether
or not she protected herself. "Look, Ellen, I've had quite a weekend myself, and I've learned way too much to explain in detail
right now." I paused, but Ellen was silent. "But the bottom line is
that I can't suggest to you more emphatically that you get yourself out of bed, go to Doylestown, and buy some smudge."

"I will when I feel better," she said stubbornly. "You don't
appreciate how sick I am."

My stomach fluttered and my chest tightened uncomfortably.
I was aghast at her steadfast refusal to listen, to protect herself.
It's her choice, I reminded myself. I needed to let it go, hope for
the best, and, most importantly of all, heed my own advice.

CHAPTER THIRTY SIX

The signs were coming at me fast and furious, but I did not want to read them. Instead, I ran away. I closed my eyes. I plunged into my files with renewed vigor and forced optimism. Between my work and my boys, I told myself, I had no time to contemplate the bizarre possibility of psychic attack. Neither did Karl. Suddenly, his trips out of town and overnight were frequent. We barely saw each other. When we did, our conversations were superficial, deliberately focussed on the mundane, the safe, the usual.

We needed to walk.

I looked at Karl from across the kitchen table and wondered at what could be happening to us. It was a Saturday morning, four weeks after my fall.

"I feel like we've become strangers," I remarked to Karl when he finally looked up at me and met my gaze. He was reading yesterday's newspaper intently—almost obsessively.

"We've been busy," snapped Karl, shrugging his shoulders. "What's the big deal? Gotta make money; gotta pay bills." He looked at me and flashed a terse, fake smile. His eyes met mine but they were cold; we didn't connect. Flicking the newspaper with both hands, he renewed his apparent fascination with the 'real' world.

"We need to take a walk," I said quietly.

"You *can't*," he snapped caustically. "Remember?"

"Hey, come on," I began, starting to get defensive. "Why are you being so mean?"

"Sorry," he said, looking me squarely in the eye, defiantly. *He looks no more sorry than the man in the moon,* I thought to myself.

"We need to talk," I said. "We need to take a walk." I looked down at my foot. It seemed okay at the moment, and I knew I could get a sneaker on. Lately, it had only been swelling by the end of the day. "We can't go on like this. We're falling apart. Let's try at least a stop sign," I suggested, referring to the shorter version of our walk, usually reserved for bitterly cold days or when we didn't have enough time to make it all the way around.

"That's a mile walk, up and back," he quickly replied. "You barely make it out to the car every day."

"Oh really?" I asked, hurt by his attitude. "Like you would even know. You've been a ghost around here, leaving at 4:30 in the morning most days and not getting home until 7:30 or later. I seem to manage to get Max to his babysitter and myself to work and the groceries bought without your help."

"Big . . . deal," he said slowly, deliberately. His eyes were cold, shut off from his heart. He'd been smoking these past weeks; I could smell it on his clothes. I wondered if he thought he was hiding it successfully. I'd promised myself that I was going to stay detached from his behavior, even though I commented on it often in my journal. There never seemed to be a time to talk about anything anyway. Our lives were a never-ending rat race.

"Please don't do this," I said simply. He was doing his best to shut me out. I moved to try to get him to look at me. I wanted him to see the pain in my eyes, the loneliness in my heart. "Why are we being this way to each other?" I asked. "Why are we fighting?"

"I don't know," admitted Karl. He closed the newspaper, which he'd been using as a shield between us, and tossed it on the table. Leaning forward, he rested his elbows on his knees and stared at the planks of the wooden floor between his feet. "I've felt so overwhelmed lately, as if I can't *do* enough." He looked up at me. "Nothing I do is good enough and I feel like all the responsibility is on me, especially since you got hurt."

"But I haven't missed a day of work! Even those few days I actually stayed at home that first week, I had files here with me and I dictated a mountain of paperwork. I've even hosted every single estate planning seminar that I'd scheduled before I was hurt! I've made it a *point* not to let my accident interfere with our lives!" I struggled to keep the edge out of my voice. All my efforts to maintain a sense of normalcy felt wasted and unappreciated.

"I'm just telling you how I *feel*," he snapped, his eyes glinting with irritation.

"OK," I said. "I'm sorry. I know I can't change the way you feel." I looked at him and cursed the tears welling up in my eyes. "But maybe, if we walk, we can sort out why you feel like it's all on you. Maybe together we can get a different perspective on what's going on with us."

"Maybe," he said grudgingly. "But I doubt it."

"It can't hurt to try," I cajoled, sensing a crack in the wall we'd allowed to be built, silently, between us. "Come on. Let's take a walk."

As we walked along our front path, we stopped to look at the tulips and late jonquils blooming in clumps throughout the garden. The buds on the magnolia tree were ready to burst and probably would today, if it got as warm as the weatherman suggested on the news last night.

Karl took a deep breath as he stepped onto the road in front of our house. "This is nice," I heard him say, but I didn't respond. It felt like he'd said it more to himself than to me. "You coming?" he asked, louder this time, as I poked around the magnolia tree inspecting the blossoms up close.

"Yup," I said, stepping cautiously onto the macadam. I noticed Karl watching me. "It feels pretty good," I said, nodding toward my foot.

"Good," he said. "Let's see how far we can get before it starts to bother you."

A minute or two of comfortable silence passed as we found a stride that my foot could handle. "Are you really angry at me?" I asked, breaking the ice. "I mean, really angry with me and resentful of our life together like you made it sound back in the kitchen?"

Karl didn't answer right away. He seemed to be taking an internal inventory. "It's hard to put into words," he began. "It's like, I feel these emotions, like a really intense anger toward you—that seems to come out of nowhere when I'm driving or laying in bed in the morning. And without really having a rational reason to feel that way, I become overwhelmed with that emotion. It's almost like I can't help it."

He stopped talking for a moment, again searching for the words to express himself. "Then I get swept up in it and my mind starts racing and thinking all these thoughts that feed my anger and resentment toward you. They make sense at the time, and justify how I feel, so I just keep dwelling on them until I'm really pissed at you and our situation and . . . everything."

I stared at the road surface before me, resisting the urge to comment. I wanted to listen. I wanted to hear what he was really saying.

"So are you *really* angry at me?" I asked again. "Are the feelings yours?"

Karl laughed. "That's a weird question." But I didn't respond. I simply continued walking, pretending to be focussed on where I was walking. I needed him to draw his own conclusions.

"When I look at things now, when I'm not in the middle of feeling all those feelings, it seems like a dream," he said, stopping in his tracks, his hands held out in a gesture of bewilderment. "It's sort of fuzzy when I try to justify now, out loud, the enormous resentment I feel toward you sometimes." We started walking again and I maintained my silence. "But it sure is intense when I'm feeling it!" he laughed uncomfortably.

"Look," I said, pointing over our heads, my finger following a red-tailed hawk as it swooped from its glide overhead to perch on top of a telephone pole just ahead of us. We stood there for a moment, like statues in the middle of the road, watching the bird preen its rich, rust-colored tail feathers.

"You're awfully quiet," Karl commented finally as we resumed our slow pace toward the stop sign. "I thought you said we needed to talk."

"We do," I agreed. "And we are. What you've told me is important." I stopped this time, turning to face him. I put my hand out and touched the lapel of his brushed cotton jacket, noticing how soft it felt. "Can you see what's going on here?" I asked, looking him straight in the eyes. "Can you see how there might be an effort on some level to separate us, to make us turn against each other?"

Recognition sparkled in Karl's eyes. It was as if a veil was being lifted from behind his eyelids. As I looked into my husband's blue-green eyes, I felt like I was finally seeing him— and he was seeing me—for the first time in a long time. "Oh, man," he said. "Do you think—?" He didn't even need to complete his sentence.

I nodded. "I think," I said firmly. "I've been getting so many signals, seeing so many signs. And I've written them down in my journal . . . but then—poof!" I snapped my fingers. "They're gone from my consciousness." I shook my head, feeling perplexed. "I don't elaborate on them. I don't string them together or draw any conclusions. It's like I forget about them or something. Or ignore them because I don't want to admit what they all add up to," I said, looking off into the distance. My foot was starting to throb.

"But you've written them down?" Karl asked. "And you haven't told me about them?"

I looked at him, my lips pursed in a smirk. "Right. With the way we've been getting along?" I snorted. "Don't you see how this all fits?"

"Well what have you been getting?" Karl asked, acting more like his old self than he had in weeks. We were at the stop sign. I could tell he wanted to go all the way around, following our usual two and a half mile trek; I did, too. But he took another look at me and could see that I was starting to hurt. Without saying a word, he reached up and touched the stop sign itself, giving it a tap and making it vibrate back and forth, our ritual when we only 'did a stop sign.' I crossed the gravel that had accumulated in little piles at the intersection of the two roads, one dirt and one paved, and tapped the sign too.

"You're being a trooper," he said, taking his hand out of his pocket and reaching for mine. "It hurts, doesn't it?" he asked as we turned and started heading back, hand in hand.

"We needed this walk," I said, deliberately ignoring his question. "And my foot needs the exercise. It's therapy," I laughed.

"Yeah, but . . . ." Karl started to protest.

"I'm just grateful I could walk this far today, you know?! It's a good start, and it shows that I'm on the road to recovery, so to speak," I said, grinning with relief at having my best friend back in sync with me. "But seriously. We have our work cut out for us from now on. We've been amazingly careless."

"I think you're right," Karl agreed.

"Now we need to go home and put it all together . . . ."

" . . . And see what needs to be seen," Karl said, finishing my thought.

CHAPTER THIRTY SEVEN

"I'm glad we didn't try to go all the way around," I said as we walked up the steps of our side porch. I didn't bother going into the house. Instead, I settled into my favorite outdoor chair and propped my throbbing foot up on the matching ottoman.

"I'll get your journal," volunteered Karl as he reached for the handle of the screen door. "Is it up beside the bed?"

"Yeah," I said. "Thanks! I appreciate it." The door slammed behind Karl and I leaned back, closing my eyes and enjoying the warm earthy smells carried by the breeze. The sunlight painted an orange sheer across the backs of my eyelids. *It's like night and day*, I thought to myself as I considered the enormous healing we'd just experienced.

"Thank You, thank You, thank You," I said out loud, grateful that my prayers had been answered.

Karl opened the screen door and leaned out, one foot in the kitchen and one foot on the porch. "Here," he said, handing me my journal. "Want a drink before I come out?"

"OK, sure!" I replied, grabbing the journal. Karl disappeared back inside. Flipping the journal open, I searched for my entry from Easter Sunday. *Just last night, I was sitting in bed feeling lonely and scared*, I thought, *wondering how everything had fallen apart between us. What made me go back and read everything I'd written since Easter? And how could I have recorded all the weird synchronicities of the past few weeks and not put them together?* I shook my head, shocked and troubled by the way I'd turned my back on the signs I'd so clearly seen along the way.

Startled, I gasped when Karl opened the door with a bang of his hip against the latch. "A little jumpy there?" he asked, laughing and handing me a tall purple glass that he'd filled with ice and lemonade. He took a sip from his turquoise one and set it on the glass-topped table in front of him. "Let me hear it," he demanded good naturedly.

I took a deep breath. "OK," I began. "I only put this all together last night," I explained. "I was sitting in bed, writing in my journal and pretty much wondering how everything could be falling apart around me. Even Ellen has withdrawn and is only coming around when she gets spooked or is feeling bad about things and wants to be cheered up. And you know how we've been," I added. "It's been awful . . . ."

"It has," Karl interrupted, agreeing with me. "I've really missed you, Lis. I'm sorry." I could feel his sincerity wrapping around me and holding me close.

"I'm sorry too," I admitted. "I wish I could have seen what was happening sooner." I took a sip of lemonade. "Anyway," I continued, "nobody's really been around for me to talk to about the things that I've been seeing. And dreaming. So it seems as though I kind of wrote them down and then forgot about them." I shook my head, puzzled. "It's just so strange that I would forget like that . . . ." I said, my voice trailing off as I tried to make sense of my lapse. I brought myself back to the present with a shake of my head. "But last night, for some reason, I went back and read all my journal entries since Easter weekend." I looked at Karl, squinting as I tried to focus on him in the bright sunlight. "I was blown away," I said seriously.

"What? What?"

"First of all, you remember what we pretty much figured out on Easter Sunday, don't you? I mean, about psychic attack and everything?"

"Yeah. Of course I do. We smudged . . . ." he began.

"Yeah, we smudged," I said. "But not very often after the first couple of days. And we certainly didn't pick up on the fact that, after a few days of not smudging, we were starting to feel angry at each other for no apparent reason, did we?"

"N-n-no," he admitted reluctantly.

"And I don't know about you but, as far as I'm concerned, as the days and weeks have gone by since my fall I've been feeling more and more fear, too. Not about anything specific, either. Just every once in a while, like as I'm driving to the grocery store, or reading a story to Max, I'll be walloped by a sudden, gut-wrenching fear in the pit of my stomach. As soon as I would feel it I'd immediately try to ignore it—and forget about it. But luckily I mentioned it in my journal several times."

Karl nodded in agreement, and I took another sip of my lemonade.

"That's how my anger toward you would hit me!" he said in amazement. "It's like I was being sent anger and you were being sent fear."

"You're right! I didn't realize, last night, that you'd been going through the same thing! That makes all of this make even more sense!" I said excitedly. "Last night, I just realized that I've been indulging in fear and anger, and getting more and more separated from you and Ellen, and I didn't even *recognize* that this is all the stuff that I'd just learned is careless and unsafe behavior. My God, it was only Easter when I learned how dangerous it is to indulge in those kind of negative thoughts!" I looked at Karl, shaken by my carelessness. "How could I have forgotten so quickly—and so completely?"

Karl returned my gaze but I could tell he was thinking about what I was saying, putting it all together for himself.

"But that's not all," I continued. "I just threw myself into my work, despite my injuries. I pretended the fall never happened. And you went along with it."

"I was running scared too," Karl admitted softly.

"I know," I said. "I'm not blaming you. I'm just observing how we each played our parts in effectively denying what was right before our eyes."

"Mm," Karl murmured, grimacing in distaste.

"And isn't it interesting that I haven't heard from Beth since that conversation on my birthday? She was going to call me the next week, she said, because she was so interested in getting together." I paused as I realized just how long it had been since I'd had any contact whatsoever with Beth or the others. "And there hasn't been any communication from Catherine, either. Not one word."

"That's OK by me," Karl said with a quick smile.

"Me too, actually," I admitted. "But something's going on here, Karl. We haven't submitted any other essays or coursework to her since our meeting in January at Beth's house. It's the beginning of May now, and we're supposed to be completing the course requirements by June. Isn't this total silence from our teacher odd? And she's psychic, clairvoyant! We know that to be true. Don't you think she probably has at least an inkling that I fell — and that I nearly died?"

Karl shifted in his seat uncomfortably. "You don't think that she—?" he cut himself off, not wanting to even give voice to his thought.

"I don't want to think it, Karl. The prospect is simply appalling." I stopped talking and just sat a moment, staring as a redheaded woodpecker furiously attacked a spot on the maple tree twenty feet away from me. "I honestly can't imagine that, knowing what she knows, she would deliberately choose to wish harm on me—or us—or anyone, for that matter. Can you?" I looked at Karl, fervently wishing he'd think of an alternative scenario that would explain our teacher's behavior.

"I don't know, Lis," he said, obviously as disturbed by this possibility as I was.

"How many times over the past couple of years have we heard Catherine repeat the warning that 'with knowledge comes responsibility?' She knows the danger of abusing power and knowledge and energy! She's lectured over and over again on the Universal Law that states that 'what you put out will come back to you ten times over.' And she has *always* stressed that the responsibility to maintain personal integrity and the highest standards is even greater if you hold yourself out as a teacher of truth!"

Neither of us said a word as we sat there contemplating the unthinkable.

"I don't want to see this, Karl. I don't want to think that Catherine could turn."

"Well, is this it? Is there anything else that's brought you to this conclusion?" I could tell he didn't want to believe it either.

"Yeah, there's more. About ten days after my fall I had a dream. I wrote it down as soon as I woke up, which was something like 4:00 a.m. or so," I said, turning the pages of my journal to locate the entry, and then reading aloud:

> *"I am driving down my parents' driveway. When I get to the bottom, I see a mountain lion out in the field ahead of me, lying down, but looking at me. The next thing I know, I've turned left and I'm suddenly walking down the road toward the neighbor's house. The field to my left is filled with lions, most of them either sitting or lying down. They roar ferociously at me and I'm afraid. But then I roar right back at them and I know I am safe."*

I looked up at Karl.

"Interesting . . . ." he commented. "But what's the significance?"

"At first I thought that it was basically a message—that if I'm afraid, I need only to roar back at those who are frightening me and I'll be safe."

"That makes sense," Karl said, nodding his head. "I get it."

"It seemed timely, too, you know? Just give it right back to them. Stand up for myself."

"Right."

"But then I looked up Mountain Lion in the Medicine Cards," I said, putting my journal on the table beside me.

"What did it say?" Karl asked.

"I only wrote down the parts that seemed to apply to me and this dream," I began, "but I can go inside and get the Medicine Card book and read you the whole thing if you want." I started to get up.

"No, that's OK," he said. "Read me what you have. I want to hear it."

"OK." I cleared my throat. "Mountain Lion stands for leadership," I said, looking at Karl.

> *"Mountain Lion can be a very difficult power totem for you to have, because it places you in a position to be a target for the problems of others. You could be blamed for things going wrong, or for always taking charge when others cannot. You could become the perfect justification for the insecurities of others. Mountain Lion medicine involves lessons on the use of power in leadership. The use and abuse of power in a position of influence are part of this great cat's medicine."*

I looked up at Karl pointedly and read that sentence again slowly. "Then get this," I said.

> *"If Mountain Lion has come to you in dreams, it is a time to stand on your convictions and lead yourself where your heart takes you."*

Can you believe that? I nearly fell over when it specifically talked about Mountain Lion coming to me in my dreams."

"That really is something," Karl agreed. "But the part about the use and abuse of power in a position of influence," Karl paused. "That's so on point . . . it's uncanny."

"And then I forgot about it! Blip! It was out of my consciousness as fast as it came. You were traveling, so I couldn't tell you that morning, and then when you got home that night," my voice trailed off as I tried to recall why I hadn't told him that evening. "Oh, I don't know, I think you may not have gotten home until late, and then you either fell asleep right after you ate or we just weren't talking to each other. Then, just yesterday, I came across that article again."

"What article?"

"The one that was in Yoga Journal."

"Yoga Journal?" Karl asked, sounding perplexed.

"Yeah, just a second," I said as I slowly got out of my chair. "Elaine let me bring it home a couple of weeks ago, remember? Let me get it." I hobbled into the kitchen, found my briefcase, and took out the magazine, returning to the porch.

"You got it at Elaine's?" Karl asked, referring to our friend, a massage therapist who had been doing therapeutic touch and some light massage on my battered body. "Oh yeah!" he said, finally. "Now I remember!"

"You've got to read this again," I said, handing him the magazine. "I think the synchronicity of having this article surface again, right in my face, pushed me over the edge. It made me realize that we have to seriously consider the possibility that Catherine has decided to play for the other team."

Karl laughed a little nervously at my attempt to make a joke. This wasn't funny; both of us knew it. But again, it just seemed impossible. This had to be a bad dream.

I sat back in my chair and closed my eyes while Karl re-read the article. My brain was tired; I didn't want to think about any of this stuff anymore. I tried focussing my attention on the birds singing in the trees surrounding the house, and faintly heard the chatter of Daniel and Max's Saturday morning cartoons filtering out from the living room.

Eventually, Karl looked up from the magazine. "This is disgusting," he said, grimacing. "I remember it now. Discrimination and discernment. It's so incredibly ironic. Catherine always emphasizes the importance of listening to our internal knowing above all else. How many times did she tell us that if something doesn't feel right or sound right, we can always vote with our feet and walk out? How many times did she lecture us about the importance of using discrimination in our search for spiritual truth and exercising discernment in deciding whether to believe anything we are taught?"

"I know," I said. "That's what makes this so hard. It's like we're being asked to use the very same tools she drilled into us as part of our metaphysical education to decide to walk away from her."

"But we can't judge it, Lisa. You know that," Karl said gently. "You read about the teachers in this article and it's not like anybody is saying that the teachings that made the person popular and powerful to begin with are a bunch of crap. Some of these spiritual teachers have had a pretty profound and positive impact on a lot of people," he said. "It looks like the power just gets to them eventually, because they're human. They're not perfect. Somehow or other they end up thinking that Universal Laws don't apply to them and that they can bend or break them every once in a while and get away with it."

"You're right," I agreed. "It's not for us to judge. They may have come into this life precisely to experience the lessons involved in facing the temptations that power provides. Who knows? They *may* have mastered all the other facets of living a human life . . . but just have this one little wrinkle to overcome." A profound sense of acceptance filled my heart. I didn't have to understand why this was happening or why certain decisions were being made by our teacher. Maybe the whys weren't for me to know. I just needed to honor what I was seeing. Believe in myself. "But the students who willingly give away their power, or allow their teachers to take their power without question, are also learning a lesson. They're learning the hard way that, no matter what, the ultimate responsibility for their safety lies with themselves."

"Exactly. It's all about paying attention and personal responsibility." He looked at me a moment, then stood up. "I love you," he said, leaning over and giving me a kiss. "I'm sorry I've been so difficult. Thanks for writing all this stuff down. I'm sure I never would have put it together if we hadn't talked it out like this."

"I'm just glad we finally talked. I love you, too."

"Well, we're in this together, you know. This is a wild ride, isn't it?"

CHAPTER THIRTY EIGHT

"D you think I should call Ellen and let her know what we suspect?" I asked Karl through the screen door about an hour later. He was planting herbs in the garden that borders the walkway, and I was making hoagies for lunch. Daniel was out behind the barn building a tree fort in our cherry tree, while Max played in the dirt beside his father.

Karl stood up and stretched. "I think so," he said. "I would want to know if the two of you figured something like that out without me." He paused. "At least I think I would," he grinned.

"I know, but it feels kind of weird, calling her up and telling her we think our teacher has turned to the dark side. It sounds so melodramatic." I half smiled at how ridiculous this all sounded to my conservative side. "Although it's not as though we haven't danced around the *possibility* that it was happening . . . ."

"Well," Karl said, "What she does with what we tell her is up to Ellen. It's her choice, you know? Just like you were telling me when you suggested that she smudge right after you fell and she got so sick. Remember?"

I nodded and smiled to myself. Most of the time I wondered just how much attention he paid to the details I often gave him when we talked about our days. But then he'd retrieve information like he just had about Ellen and surprise the heck out of me. "So you think I should call her?" I confirmed.

"Yeah, I think it's time we ended our relationship with Catherine, don't you?"

"I don't think we can allow it to continue, knowing what we know," I said. "Or at least believing what we believe," I added. "I think it only seems right for us to let Ellen in on it and see if she agrees."

An hour and a half later, Ellen was sitting on our porch, listening wide-eyed as we filled her in on what we'd put together. "Catherine's still talking to me," she said when we were finished. "At least I think she is," she added after a moment. "I sent in my answers to another course last week, but I haven't heard from her that she even got it."

"So are you planning on going through with the ordination?" I asked, surprised and feeling a bit more guarded than I had before. I was struggling to remain detached, but it wasn't easy. Ellen seemed so willing to pretend that everything was still the same between all of us. I knew that she and Beth were still in touch with each other and, after my fall, I specifically asked Ellen to leave me completely out of any conversations she might have with her. Ellen assured me that I had not come up in the one or two times she'd spoken with Beth over the past couple of weeks, but that in and of itself struck me as a bit odd.

"I don't think so," she said, as though pondering aloud. "I'm totally turned off by all the religious implications that come up for me when I hear the word *ordination*. But I've worked so long and so hard on my course work that it's almost a shame not to at least complete that," she said, almost more to herself than to Karl and me. "Are you guys going to participate in the ordination?"

I looked at her in disbelief. "I don't think so," I said, maybe a little too sarcastically. *Isn't she listening to what we're saying?* "Why don't you read that article on spiritual teachers while I get us some chips," I suggested.

"OK," she agreed.

After several minutes Ellen looked up from the article in her hands. Karl was sitting in my chair and Ellen and I were sharing the glider. "You guys really think that Catherine is abusing her power?"

I shrugged and Karl said nothing. "Maybe," I said. "But I've reached the point where I've got to trust myself. I don't have a good feeling about this anymore. I don't know what's going on with Catherine or Beth or anybody else. Maybe there's nothing to it and it's all a figment of my imagination. Maybe I'm not seeing clearly at all. But one thing I do know is that Catherine has always maintained that if something doesn't feel right to you inside," I said, pointing to my chest, "then you should vote with your feet. So, for all the reasons I've just given you, as well as everything I told you right after I fell and then had confirmed when I read that *Shouting at the Wolf* book, I'm not going to be involved in the ordination ceremony."

"Neither am I," added Karl.

"And quite frankly, I don't think Catherine has any interest whatsoever in having me complete my studies with her, either. The silence toward me is deafening."

"That is peculiar," agreed Ellen.

"Us, rather," I corrected myself. "Although I don't feel as though there is as much animosity toward Karl as there is toward me. I don't know why," I mused. "Maybe I'm just paranoid," I laughed.

"Yeah, you just want to be the center of attention," teased Karl.

"That's right! Hate thoughts, love thoughts, doesn't matter to me." I stuck my tongue out at Karl, then turned to Ellen. "Seriously, though, we just wanted to let you know what we think is going on and how we intend to deal with it," I continued. "Whatever you do is up to you."

"Well I don't want to be involved if there's something dark going on," she began. "But how are we going to get out of it? I've already been called by Brenda to help get things ready for the ceremony."

"Me too," I confirmed. Karl looked at me in surprise. I nodded my head, my lips set in a grim line. "She left a message on our answering machine last week," I said. "I'm going to have to call her tomorrow and beg off. Like I said, I doubt that this will come as much of a surprise to any of them *in reality*," I emphasized. "There's no doubt in my mind that they know what's going on and that we've figured it out."

"Are you going to tell her why you don't want to be involved any more?" Ellen asked.

"I'm going to say as little as possible. Let's face it. They don't want me around; and I don't want to be around them. Not to mention that I strongly suspect that they've tried to hurt me and disrupt our marriage." I glanced at Karl and shook my head, laughing softly but feeling little humor in the situation. "I don't owe them any explanations—or any revelations about how much I may or may not know about what's really going on."

"Sounds like a plan to me!" Karl said enthusiastically.

"Did I tell you that I thought *you* should call Brenda back?" I asked him with a straight face.

"Aw, come on," he said. "No way!"

"I'm kidding. I'll do it. You big baby," I added.

Ellen looked scared. She'd known Catherine the longest of any of us, and I felt compassion for her ambivalence. I didn't want to believe our teacher could be abusing her power, either. I was still struggling with it in my head, but my heart told me it was time to listen. It seemed harder for Ellen, though.

"Why don't we pick a rune on this whole thing?" I suggested. "Maybe they will help cut through all our emotional coloring and help us tap into a deeper insight on the situation."

"OK," Karl and Ellen agreed.

Ellen chose first. She sat with the bag of runes in her hand and held the issue in her mind, silently asking for guidance. Reaching in with her left hand, she drew one out. "Movement reversed," she said. "Hmmph," she snorted, "Sounds like I'm not supposed to do something, huh?"

I looked in the table of contents, found Movement, and read her the rune. She looked uneasy. "Read me that last part again?" she asked.

> " . . . *We have simply to recognize that not all opportunities are appropriate, that not all possibilities are open to us. The opportunity at hand may be precisely to avoid action.*"

I looked up. "That part?" I asked her.

"Yeah," she replied. She was silent for a moment. "You pick," she said to Karl, chucking the bag of runes into his lap.

Karl sat holding the bag and, eventually, reached in and picked a rune. "Opening reversed," he said, looking at me.

> "*Expect a darkening of the light in some situation or relationship. A friendship may be dying, a partnership, a marriage, some aspect of yourself that is no longer appropriate to the person you are now. Receiving this Rune puts you on notice that failure to face up to the death consciously would constitute a loss of opportunity. Kano is one of the Cycle Runes. Reversed, it points to the death of a way of life invalidated by growth. Reversed, this Rune calls for giving up gladly the old, and being prepared to live for a time empty: It calls for developing inner stability—not being seduced by the momentum of old ways while waiting for the new to become illuminated in its proper time.*"

"Well that's pretty clear," he said. He tossed the bag to me. "Your turn, deary."

"Watch," I joked. "I'll pick a rune that tells me to follow the leader or something." Inside, I cringed. *Their runes were so clear, so unequivocal*, I thought to myself. *What if I do get something that says my instincts are all wrong?*

262 | LISA JG WEIKEL

"Are you going to pick?" Karl asked, interrupting my paranoid reverie.

"Yeah, yeah. Hold your horses." I sat and cleared my mind,
holding the rune bag in my left hand. I swirled the stones with
my fingers through the outside of the pouch, mixing them, mixing them, until it felt right to stop. I reached in and chose the first
stone that jumped into my hand. "Initiation reversed," I stated.

We looked at each other and laughed.

"Looks like we're three for three," I said.

That night, I sat on our bed, my journal in my lap. Karl was
sound asleep, but I had yet to record the distance we'd traveled.
The title itself of the rune I'd chosen was a simple and obvious
confirmation of our decision. But the wording of the rune's interpretation cut deep and had many levels of meaning. Sensing an
inner urgency to truly 'get' the message, I tried to internalize it
by copying the words into my journal:

> "*You simply cannot repeat the old and not suffer.
> (. . .) You may feel overwhelmed with exhaustion from
> meeting obstruction after obstruction in your passage. Yet
> you always have a choice: You can see all this apparent
> negativity as 'bad luck,' or you can recognize it as an
> obstacle course, a challenge specific to the Initiation you
> are presently undergoing. Then each setback, each hu-
> miliation, becomes a test of character. When your inner
> being is shifting and reforming on a deep level, patience,
> constancy and perseverance are called for. So stay cen-
> tered, see the humor, and keep on keeping on.*"

CHAPTER THIRTY NINE

The next morning, I decided to grab the bull by the horns and call Brenda first thing. She was cordial and sweet over the phone, and when I vaguely described my discomfort with the whole ordination issue, she replied that if we weren't *right* with it, then we should listen to ourselves. It took a few more minutes before I realized that she still assumed we would be attending the gathering.

"We aren't going to be available to help set up," I explained, trying to phrase it as delicately as possible. "And we won't be attending the presentations or the ceremonies, either. We're going to be out of town that weekend," I said. As part of our final project, we were each supposed to prepare an in-depth discourse on our choice of any esoteric subject. A significant element of the graduation weekend was to be the exhibition of our findings to our fellow students, past graduates of the program who were coming in from all over the country, and members of the public.

"So you're not going to participate at all?" she asked, a distinct edge creeping into her voice. "Karl either?"

"No, it's just not right for us at this time," I said, trying to be truthful but not wanting to go into the details.

"You should speak with Anna." Anna—the only other person in the entire organization who might have more power than Catherine. At the very least, she was Catherine's equal. We'd met her personally only a couple of times over the years, before we'd even begun formal study with Catherine. I knew her more from listening to the school's teaching tapes, which had been made several years earlier, when the school had had far more students enrolled and more frequent lectures. "If you have a talk with her, then maybe you and Karl can arrange to be ordained privately, in Vermont, when you feel you're ready," advised Brenda.

No thanks, was my initial, unspoken, reaction. But as the conversation continued, the prospect of speaking with Anna appealed to me more and more. I thought it might give me a chance to leave with fewer hard feelings. I asked Brenda for the number at least three times during the remainder of the conversation, but each time she seemed ready to give it to me, she got sidetracked or just plain seemed to forget. It wasn't until I hung up the phone that I realized I still didn't have Anna's number.

"That seemed to go OK," remarked Karl, who'd listened to my end of the conversation as he sat at the kitchen table with me.

"It went all right," I acknowledged. "She wasn't happy that we weren't going to be helping set up, though." I picked up a pencil that was lying on the table and started nervously flicking it back and forth against the tabletop. "She suggested, repeatedly, that I call and speak to Anna."

"You're not going to, are you?" Karl asked, sounding surprised that I'd even consider calling her.

"Well, yeah," I stuttered. "I didn't think it would hurt to see what she has to say." Karl looked at me doubtfully. "It's not like she's going to change my mind or anything," I said, sensing his disapproval.

"I don't see why you would want to talk to her at all," he said, shaking his head.

"Just because Catherine may have turned doesn't mean Anna has," I stated.

"That's true," Karl conceded.

"And she was always particularly friendly and nice to us," I added. "It was like we'd always known each other or something."

Karl smiled. "I remember. She was a really nice lady."

"No need to worry, though," I said, shrugging my shoulders as I dismissed the whole idea. "For all the times she suggested I speak with her, Brenda never did give me her number."

Two hours later I found myself sitting at my desk in my office, the door closed. I was tempted to try to find Anna's number, to see if she would say anything to me that might change my mind or help me see things from a different perspective. I decided to pick a rune on my day first. Maybe that would help me decide whether I should continue my search or simply let it go.

Lifting the rune pouch from my briefcase, I held them in my hand and tried to hold the general feeling of the situation in my mind. I asked for guidance, pure and simple.

Drawing the rune out of the bag, my breath caught in my throat. *Hagalaz.*

Spooked, I told myself I'd steer clear of any creeks and watch my attitude. In an effort to distract myself, I decided to call information to see if I could track down Anna's number on my own. It was unlisted. Suddenly, the name and face of a former graduate of the program, Marcia, popped into my head. I'd met Marcia at a seminar a few years before, but run into her a couple of times since then at various Catherine-related functions. She'd recently moved to Nashville, but for some reason, I'd recorded her number in my address book. I decided to give her a call.

"Marcia?" I asked when a woman's voice answered the telephone.

"Yes," came the hesitant reply. "May I help you?"

I proceeded to introduce myself and remind her of the details of the last time we'd met.

"Oh sure!" she said warmly, her voice mellowing to the distinct, rich quality I remembered. "Of course. You came with your husband, didn't you?"

"Yes," I laughed, amused that we were remembered as a couple. "Karl."

"That's right, of course I remember you."

"Are you coming to the ordination that's planned for the solstice?" I asked, trying to make small talk before asking for Anna's number. I fully expected her to say she'd be attending.

"No, I won't be able to," she said. "I can't leave my business right now, since we're just getting on our feet and everything."

"Oh!" I said, surprised. I hesitated. "We won't be going either," I volunteered. "In fact, I just talked to Brenda this morning to tell her that we won't be participating at all and she suggested that I contact Anna." I paused, waiting to see what Marcia would say, but she was silent. "She forgot to give me Anna's number, so I thought I'd call to see if you have it."

"You're not going to participate at all?" she asked, sounding surprised herself. "You and Karl are studying with Catherine, aren't you?"

"Well . . .," I hesitated, " . . . We were." I didn't know what else to say. I didn't want to elaborate. I knew that the best policy was silence. "It's just not working out right now. We're both so busy with our work and everything that we're finding it hard to give our studies the attention they require." It sounded lame to my ears, but I tried to sound convincing.

Nevertheless, before I knew it, our conversation became more personal and I found out that Marcia herself had recently resigned from the church. Her revelation was completely unexpected. Sensing her reluctance to disclose the reasons behind her decision, I began cautiously outlining the conclusions Karl and I had reached, as well as the circumstantial evidence that supported them. Every single suspicion we'd had was confirmed or corroborated by Marcia, either through direct knowledge or her own experience. When I told her the details of my fall, her reaction was emphatic.

"You must protect yourselves," she said. "You are right, this is a matter of life and death, and you are dealing with something that is dark. Very dark." Her tone had gone from friendly to ominous in minutes. She gave me very few details of her own encounter and falling out with Catherine, and I asked for none. I didn't want to know. I knew there was more there than I wanted to know, and I knew I didn't need to know. "It is a grave and serious matter when a Teacher—and I say that with a capital 'T,'" she interjected, "makes a conscious choice to turn to the dark side. She will do anything she can to protect herself if she thinks she's been discovered."

I felt like I'd been punched in the gut. "Oh no," I said. "Oh my." My voice sounded soft and far away, as if it wasn't even coming from my body. There was that buzz again — the same one as when the Indian had told me to *know myself.*

"You must not give in to fear," she said, eerily repeating the words I myself had written in my journal only the night before. Words I'd first written on Easter Sunday.

"I know," I said, starting to regain some composure.

"You must—and I cannot emphasize this enough—you *must* remain centered and balanced and keep love in your hearts. You must not become preoccupied with fear! Watch your thoughts like a hawk and keep them happy and light."

"This is real, isn't it?" I asked dumbly, wishing she would break into laughter and tell me it was all a silly prank; a practical joke with a metaphysical twist.

"I hate to tell you this, but this is all too real," she said, sorrow clearly audible in her voice, even over the telephone. "But you can't get wrapped up in feeling sorry for what *is*," she said, pulling herself up by her spiritual bootstraps and encouraging me to do likewise. "You just have to deal with it. We all do, sooner or later." Marcia sighed and I could tell it was a struggle for her to remain detached about this as well, despite her admonition to me. "Everyone makes choices. It's not for us to judge anyone else's choices, even if we know without a doubt in the world that they will only lead to darkness."

"But I can't believe that someone who knows as much about power and karma, for heaven's sake, would make a choice like this!" I declared, wanting Marcia to explain how this could possibly be happening.

"I know," she said. "It is beyond comprehension. But I'm telling you . . .," again, her voice became stronger, more confident, "you must forget about the choices others may or may not have made and focus on keeping your own thoughts light and loving. You must do whatever it takes to protect yourself and your family." She paused. "Do you know how to protect yourself?"

"Well, I have a book that I've been reading that gives a lot of suggestions. And we've smudged a couple of times," I added. "And I've been trying to keep my thoughts positive, although it's weird how suddenly I'll find myself feeling anger and fear for no reason at all . . . ."

"Yes, that's common when you're under attack," she interrupted. I groaned to myself. She even used the words I kept trying to avoid: *Under attack.*

"I will send you some books to read that will help you out. But in the meantime, it is important that you start some specific forms of protection right away. One is to say the following prayer as often as you can. Whenever you think about that person—or any of the people associated with her—make a point of saying this aloud, if possible:

By the presence that I am

This attachment shall cease to be,

Now and forever.

Almighty I AM, Almighty I AM, Almighty I AM."

I wrote the prayer down. My hand was shaking. "Is there anything else I should know?" I asked. "I'm assuming all prayers are powerful, right?"

"Yes," she confirmed. "Another thing. Don't speak her name any more. There is power in speaking a person's name, and you don't want to give her any more power than she already has. Speaking her name creates an energetic connection that could call her attention to you as well." She paused. "Have you bought any jewelry from her?"

My heart sank. "Yes, a couple of rings and things over the years," I began. "And a beautiful carved totem necklace I bought about six months ago."

"Have you been wearing it a lot?"

"Not lately," I replied, surprised that I hadn't thought about my necklace for quite a while. "I haven't worn it in a couple of months, actually. Since I came back from New Mexico! Every time I put it on I'd feel a burning sensation at the top of my back. It became so irritating that I couldn't keep it on for more than a few minutes at a time. Eventually, I just stopped wearing the piece all together."

"I'm not surprised," she said. "Listen to me. This is very important. You must cleanse and demagnetize all of the jewelry you bought from her—or even any jewelry or stones or crystals she may have simply touched." As soon as she said this, I flashed back to our last get together, when we'd had our oral examinations. The summer before, I'd given Karl a tourmaline for his birthday. Since we'd returned from New Mexico, he'd worn the gem and his Warrior's Wisdom key together, on the same chain. During that weekend, however, when we were at Beth's home, Catherine had held the tourmaline in both her hands, purportedly to bless it. Within days, he'd felt a sharp clash between the objects hanging around his neck and decided to remove the brass key from the chain. Almost immediately, Karl was back to sneaking cigarettes, lying about it, and generally becoming more and more irritable and out of balance. Not until this moment had I put the two events together.

"Are you OK?" asked Marcia.

"Yes, yes. I was just thinking. What should I do with all that jewelry?"

"Bury it."

"Excuse me?"

"Bury it. The earth will cleanse the jewelry and remove all

negative energy that may be attached to it—if you ask for help. Sea salt is also a great energetic cleanser, but for this situation I would recommend asking Mother Earth for assistance."

"Alright. I can do that," I murmured, copiously writing down her instructions.

"But you must also get rid of anything else you might have in your possession that you received from her or anyone else you think may be involved with her. When you have reason to believe a person may be attacking you psychically—regardless of whether *they* are conscious of the power of thought or not—you must be vigilant to sever any connections to that individual. And that includes any gifts you've received or objects you've borrowed from them," she added. "Take steps to cleanse and purify them, if they're worth it, or just dispose of them completely if they're not."

I remembered reading something similar in *Shouting at the Wolf*, but I guess, despite everything, I'd still resisted how amazingly connected we all are energetically. Why hadn't I thought to apply it to my own life? It seemed like too much work, maybe. Or too paranoid. Or maybe I just didn't want to accept the responsibility that was landing on my shoulders if I did indeed accept the premise that our thoughts and words have power and that we can take steps to protect ourselves from the unconsciousness—or worse, the malicious intent—of others.

"OK," I said. I wanted to throw up. I'd never in my wildest dreams expected to have such a conversation when I made this call.

"And there is one more thing you need to know," Marcia said gently.

"What's that?"

"Nothing is more powerful than the Light. Know that with every fiber of your being and never forget it."

"OK," I said simply.

"I'll pray for you. Make sure you pray for yourselves. Be silent and careful. And keep love in your heart."

"I will. Thank you for being honest with me," I said. "I know you took a risk by telling me the truth."

"Ah!" she laughed. "You're right. But the truth shall set you free!"

On my way home that afternoon, I found myself sitting fourth in line at a stoplight. My ears perked up when I heard the same smooth, rumbling growl distinctive to the exhaust system of my car coming from somewhere ahead of me. Straining forward in my seat, I could see the outline of a vehicle the same make and model as mine, sitting at the front of the line I was in, waiting for the light to change. I don't often see many cars like mine, yet much to my surprise, this one was even the same color as my own. As the two lanes of traffic on our side of the road accelerated, the faded red pickup truck and blue Taurus which were between us moved over into the right lane. I pulled up closer, noticing that the car in front of me was indeed *identical* to mine.

Then my heart stopped as I squinted at the car's license plate, not believing my eyes: "BLC MJC."

"Black magic!?" I gasped out loud, a sliver of terror shooting through me like an icy lightning bolt. I immediately began reciting out loud the prayer Marcia had given me, saying it over and over again, each time making an effort to state the words with more courage and confidence than the last. I pictured myself safe and protected, with a blanket of pure loving energy wrapped around me and my vehicle.

Black magic. Something tickled at the back of my mind. Despite the initial jolt of fear caused by such a strange synchronicity, I noticed that I felt okay. I felt protected and strong. As my car-twin pulled into the left hand turning lane, and I passed by it without getting a glimpse of the driver, it dawned on me that what I'd just experienced had not been a threat. I'd been given the key to the mystery.

A bubble of memory suddenly percolated into my consciousness as I remembered where I'd seen a reference to black magic a long time ago. I'd buried it so deep that even my Easter realization and my reading of *Shouting at the Wolf* hadn't jogged it loose. At least, not until now.

And now the discovery of my upside down Owl, and everything that had occurred since then, made perfect sense.

CHAPTER FORTY

An hour later, Karl and I were digging a hole in our back yard, burying various rings, the moonstone Catherine had said would 'open me up,' Karl's tourmaline . . . and, of course, the magnificent totem necklace. We'd set upon completing this cleansing task as soon as I'd told Karl about my incredible conversation with Marcia.

"This all started when I bought this, you know," I said, holding the necklace in my hands and rubbing my fingers over the bear at its center. "I was wearing it when we found the owl. Remember how sure I was that the bird was bringing me a message?" I laughed and shook my head.

"Didn't we read the Medicine Card for Owl back then?" Karl asked, glancing at the Medicine Card book tucked under my left arm.

"Not right away," I replied, shaking my head. We didn't have the cards when we first found the owl."

"But we must have looked it up eventually?" he asked, lifting the shovel out of the hole and leaning on it, his hands cupped over the end of the handle.

"You're right; we must have. Although for the life of me, I can't remember exactly when." I closed my eyes, vainly trying to will the memory back into my consciousness. Opening my eyes again, I shrugged my shoulders. "But when I saw that license plate today, everything fell into place and the owl's message hit me squarely between the eyes. I suddenly recalled the words from Owl Reversed—and I remembered how revolted I'd felt by the whole idea of dark arts and black magic. I must have put the words out of my head as soon as I read them. They didn't fit into my belief about reality—and I didn't *want* them to, either."

"Tell me," prodded Karl. "I don't remember."

"Listen to this," I said, laying the necklace on the grass and opening the jade cover of the Medicine Card book to the section on Owl. Skipping to the second page, where one single paragraph conveyed more information than I was willing to accept so many months ago, I began reading:

> *"If you have Owl upside-down in your cards, you have been greatly deceived by either yourself or another. Perhaps witchcraft or black magic is being used against you, or maybe you are using witchcraft or sorcery to aid you when you should be praying and asking the Great Spirit for guidance. The message is to befriend the darkness inside yourself. Look deeply, and soon the bright light of dawn will illuminate you. Then ask yourself what you are in the dark about. How and by whom are you being deceived? Have you lied to yourself about someone or something? Are you being greatly deceived, or just slightly deceived? Owl tells you to keep an eye on your property and your loved ones. Remember that Owl is always asking, "Who?""*

I looked at Karl, waiting for his reaction. Fiery beams of sunlight pushed through the tangled branches of our neighbors' trees weaving an intricate crosshatch of shadow and light on the grass beneath our feet. Only the totem necklace was immersed in a puddle of pure orange light, as if even the sun was doing its part to cleanse the powerful object before it was buried in the earth.

"Wow. It's taken you all this time to accept that you have Owl medicine. But you've got to wonder if *she* didn't know all along—after you discovered the owl—that you would see in the dark, that you would discover the deception and recognize that she had turned." Karl laughed at the irony. "Maybe it was your destiny to see what you've seen, and help us accept that both Light *and* Darkness exist. You can't protect yourself against something that you don't believe exists."

"Hmm," I grunted thoughtfully as I contemplated this perspective.

"You *asked* her to be your teacher, remember?"

"Yes," I said, smiling now at the memory. "And I couldn't understand why she hesitated to take us on. I was so hurt." I stared at the totem necklace laying in the grass, not really seeing it, absorbed in my memories.

"Let's do it," Karl declared, dragging my awareness back to our task.

I reached for the smudge stick that Karl had brought out earlier and placed in the grass, and lit it with the wooden matches from my pocket. Speaking from my heart, I cleansed each of the objects in the sacred smoke and blessed the earthen hollow Karl had created for their burial. We covered the jewelry with dirt and prayed for the protection of ourselves and our family.

"You know what I feel right now?" I asked Karl as we tamped down the last piece of sod.

"No," Karl replied quietly. "What?"

"Gratitude. As awful as this has been, I can see how it was meant to be; that somehow, on some level, Catherine *agreed* to teach us these lessons, and we agreed—no, *asked*, to learn them. Maybe this whole experience was the only way she felt capable of driving home the lesson of discernment—and teaching me to trust my gift of owl medicine."

A few weeks later, I wake up in our bed, sweating, yet cold with fright. I look at the red glow of the numbers on our clock-radio: 3:30 a.m. Reaching for my journal, I grab a pen from my nightstand and begin to write out my dream, quickly, before it dissolves:

> *"Karl and I are at the hotel where we attended the seminar in January. I am having a discussion with some-one who discloses that they've told Catherine more about me than I'd hoped. Suddenly, Catherine approaches Karl and me and confronts us, anger and hate seething from her very being. She walks away and I throw something at her, accusing her of working black magic and telling her she can't hide it from me any more. She whirls around, faces me, and despite my terror, I glare right back at her, standing my ground."*

Dropping the journal and pen to the floor and switching off the light, I stare into the darkness, reliving the dramatic emotions of my dream, realizing, deep down, that I've *finally* passed the test. Over and over, prayers of protection echo through my mind as I dance between dreaming and wakefulness.

Thank you, Catherine. Thank you for being my teacher.

EPILOGUE

Without a doubt, the word *evil* is probably one of the most emotionally 'loaded' words tossed about nowadays, particularly in our culture. Even my editor became testy when she found herself struggling to identify with my feelings, thoughts and discoveries regarding this concept. In fact, her irritation with my use of the word *evil* engendered lengthy email correspondence and a particularly extensive telephone conversation between us, all of which, she hoped, would persuade me to reconsider my word choice.

As can be seen, however, I refused to cave in to her editorial pressure and insisted upon keeping the word—and concept of—evil as an integral facet of this book. In deference to my editor, however, I am writing this Epilogue to clarify my motives.

It is not my intention, in writing this book, to persuade anyone to give *evil* the same definition as I have. However, it is my hope that *Owl Medicine* will provoke passionate, articulate, discussion and, most importantly, raise AWARENESS of evil's existence in the world—as well as reinforce the power we all have to make choices that either foster or thwart it.

There is a clamoring within us all to make sense of the coldhearted brutality that seems to be encroaching more and more upon our personal lives and collective consciousness. Yet the finger-pointing extends ever outward, distracting us from examining how we, as individuals, unwittingly perpetuate evil by refusing to take responsibility for our unconsciousness and ignorance.

With knowledge comes power . . . and we must, each of us, choose awareness, accept responsibility, step into our power, and use that power wisely.

Books of Interest

Akhilananda, Swami. *Spiritual Practices*. Boston: Branden Press, 1972.

Anderson, Reed. *Shouting at the Wolf: A Guide to Identifying and Warding Off Evil in Everday Life*. New York: Citadel Press, 1990. Out of Print.

Andrews, Lynn V. *Medicine Woman*. San Francisco: Harper & Row, 1983.

Flight of the Seventh Moon: The Teaching of the Shields. San Francisco: Harper & Row, 1984.

Jaguar Woman and the Wisdom of the Butterfly Tree. San Francisco: Harper & Row, 1985.

Teachings Around the Sacred Wheel: Finding the Soul of the Dreamtime. San Francisco: Harper & Row, 1990.

Auel, Jean. *Clan of the Cave Bear*. New York: Bantam Books, 1984.

Blavatsky, Helena. *An Abridgement of The Secret Doctrine*. Wheaton, Ill.: The Theosophical Publishing House, 1967.

Blum, Ralph. *The Book of Runes*. New York: St. Martin's Press, 1993.

Campbell, Joseph. *Hero With a Thousand Faces*. Princeton: Princeton University Press, 1990.

Castaneda, Carlos. *The Teachings of Don Juan: A Yaqui Way of Knowledge*. New York: Ballantine Books, 1968.

A Separate Reality: Further Conversations With Don Juan. New York: Simon and Schuster, 1971.

Journey to Ixtlan: The Lessons of Don Juan. New York: Simon and Schuster, 1972.

Tales of Power. New York: Washington Square Press, 1974.

The Second Ring of Power. New York: Washington Square Press, 1977.

The Eagle's Gift. New York: Washington Square Press, 1981.

The Power of Silence. New York: Washington Square Press, 1987.

Cranston, Sylvia, and Head, Joseph. *Reincarnation: The Phoenix Fire Mystery.* New York: Julian Press, Inc., 1977.

Reincarnation: an East-West Anthology, including quotations from the world's religions and from over 400 Western thinkers. Wheaton, IL: Theosophical Publishing House, 1985.

Haich, Elisabeth. *Initiation.* Redway, California: Seed Center, 1974.

Hall, Manly P. *The Secret Teachings of All Ages.* Los Angeles: The Philosophical Research Society, Inc., 1977.

Reincarnation: The Cycle of Necessity. The Philosophical Research Society, Inc., 1939, 1967.

King, Godfre Ray. *Unveiled Mysteries.* Mount Shasta, CA: Ascended Master Teaching Foundation, 1986.

The Magic Presence. Schaumberg, IL: Saint Germaine Press, Inc., 1963.

"I AM" Discourses. Schaumberg, IL: Saint Germaine Press, Inc., 1940.

MacLaine, Shirley. *Out on a Limb.* New York: Bantam Books, 1986.

Going Within: A Guide for Inner Transformation. New York: Bantam Books, 1989.

Millman, Daniel. *Way of the Peaceful Warrior.* Tiburon, CA: H J Kramer, Inc., 1984.

Roberts, Jane. *The Nature of Personal Reality: A Seth Book.* San Rafael, CA: Amber-Allen Publishing, 1994.

Roman, Sanaya. *Living With Joy: Keys to Personal Power and Spiritual Transformation (Book I of the Earth Life Series).* Tiburon, CA: H J Kramer, Inc., 1986.

Personal Power Through Awareness: A Guidebook for Sensitive

People (Book II of the Earth Life Series). Tiburon, CA: H J Kramer, Inc., 1986.

Spiritual Growth: Being Your Higher Self (Book III of the Earth Life Series). Tiburon, CA: H J Kramer, Inc. 1989.

Wilde, Stuart. *"The Taos Quartet":*

Miracles. Taos, NM: White Dove International, Inc., 1983. (Reprint edition, Carlsbad, CA: Hay House, Inc., 1998).

The Force. Taos, NM: White Dove International, Inc., 1985.(Reprint edition, Carlsbad, CA: Hay House, Inc., 1995).

Affirmations. Taos, NM: White Dove International, Inc., 1987.(Reprint edition, Carlsbad, CA: Hay House, Inc., 1995).

The Quickening. Taos, NM: White Dove International, Inc., 1988.(Reprint edition, Carlsbad, CA: Hay House, Inc., 1995).

Yogananda, Paramahansa. *Autobiography of a Yogi*. Los Angeles: Self-Realization Fellowship, 1985.

Printed in the United States
2645